THE BRIDPORT

POETRY, SHORT STORIES AND

JUDGES
Monica Ali • Short Stories and Flash Fiction
Daljit Nagra • Poetry

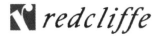

First published in 2018 by Redcliffe Press Ltd
81g Pembroke Road, Bristol BS8 3EA

e: info@redcliffepress.co.uk
www.redcliffepress.co.uk
Follow us on Twitter @RedcliffePress

Follow The Bridport Prize:
Follow us on Twitter @BridportPrize
www.bridportprize.org.uk
www.facebook.com/bridportprize

ISBN 978-1-911408-36-9

British Library Cataloguing-in-Publication Data
A catalogue record for this book is available from the British Library

Typeset in 10.5pt Times

Typeset by Addison Print Ltd, Northampton
Printed by Hobbs the Printers Ltd, Totton

Contents

Poetry Report   Daljit Nagra   5
Short Story Report   Monica Ali   8
Flash Fiction Report   Monica Ali   10

Exhibition   John Freeman   13
what we learn from movies about surviving a nuclear blast
   Luisa A. Igloria   15
The Act of Dinner   Ashish Xiangyi Kumar   16
Atonement   Patricia Cantwell   17
Mirror, Mirror, On the Wall   Emily Chen   18
Memory (Potacari)   Heather Derr-Smith   19
Cliff Top Trail   Melissa Goodbourn   20
Curations   Vanessa Lampert   22
In Japan   Jenni Mazaraki   23
Now and Then   Kevin McCarthy   24
Space was a material   Simon Middleton   25
Burial Chambers   Mark Paffard   27
Reversal   Sam Phipps   28
Trading Armadillos   Alison Thompson   29
The Fore Caddie   V. Sanjay Kumar   30
The Heartsick Diaspora   Elaine Chiew   40
Wet Bloody Country   Gerry McKeague   52
Crossing   Karen Ashe   63
Karolina   Aifric Campbell   70
Black Boys   Catherine Chidgey   73
Digging   Patrick Doddy   85
Beckett in the Woods   Daniel Lambert   92
Four Corners   Chetna Maroo   96
Variation of Molly   Corrina O'Beirne   105
Ouroboros   Ryan O'Connor   118
Near Llandaff   Ranjit Saimbi   125
Likes   Sara Sherwood   129
The Grand Finale   Tim Craig   135
Nan   Jim Gleeson   136
What Real Men Wished They Dreamed   Molia Dumbleton   137
Lucky Underpants   Ruth Brandt   138
Partial   Elizabeth Edelglass   139
Courtship   Emma Neale   140

Biographies   141

DALJIT NAGRA

Poetry Report

Being invited to hear someone's revelations or considered reflections is always a moment of great privilege and responsibility. Suddenly the world feels so sensitive and serious, because the listener will be keeping that moment to themselves, or taking away an admission that might well revive them in some way. Poetry too is that frank conversation with an assumed other who cares to hear us out. Judging a poetry competition feels a communal, a social and a moral act, where we are at our best and ready to receive. I love this aspect of judging a poetry prize, that it will bring out the best in me for the way I attend to each poem, for the way I will leave the room of the poems enriched, and above all, that I will be able to share those riches with the audience of the prize.

I have hugely enjoyed judging the Bridport Prize. So many moments of revelation and insight came my way, and from all the conversations I listened to, I have selected my winners. Many good poems missed out and several of the winning poems could have been more successful; as a judge, it's difficult to know what unconscious forces have guided your selection. I have tried my best to be objective and merit the best crafted, the moments of greatest insight or artful play, that the poems felt they matched form to content with effective tension, that the poems felt the right length, while surprising me with the journey they had taken from beginning to end, and that there has been an imaginative and intellectual ambition which has carried the poem across its distance. Perhaps most of all, memorability is the key guide, that strange combination of acoustic, symbolic, phrase making and other elements that go into creating a fresh world of rumination, and that has stayed vividly me for days after first reading that poem. I hope many of the winning poems will stay vividly with me much longer than the duration of the judging period.

My only sadness, that some poems could have done better but for the occasional typo which hampered my reading experience; I had to judge what was in front me. I had to assume that the poem, as it lay before me, was in the exact form as the poet had wished it.

The Highly Commended poems are 'Atonement' – a stunning poem of convinced displacement. The blanket is not really a blanket but an unborn child. Superb exploration of trauma and re-enactment. 'Burial

Chambers' – the pub scene is apt for a poem about the passing of cultures, where closeness and distance vie, and where the past, though sunk under, remains alive. An exciting and hopeful poem. 'Cliff Top Trail' has superb lineation, vivid images and an ideal setting to dramatise potential hope in a poem where the speaker is in utter abandonment. The form and the sensuality cleverly offer hope against the despair. 'Curations' – the second person pronoun helps distance the shocking news as each moment of the revelation is minutely recalled. A heart-breaking and vividly sustained poem. 'In Japan' is a vivid exploration of loneliness that pushes the prose-poem to exciting new possibilities. The dense form builds up the feeling of being elsewhere and not wanted. An unforgettable poem.

In 'Memory (Potacari)' – the past is revisited in a testament to the dead of Srebenica. The powerful rhetoric makes for a poignant and wise poem about loss and ritual. 'Mirror, Mirror, On the Wall is a rhythmically propelled and powerful drama about the female body in its individual and traditional states. Politically complex and compact. 'Now and Then' is beautifully gentle in style, capturing the sensual world and how it exists and is denied through its glorious paradoxes. This is a delicate and exciting poem. 'Reversal' – the disarming simplicity and ordinary setting suit the compact yet psychologically complex memory. The pronoun 'you' is well-achieved in tight quatrains about healing and ultimately redemption. 'Trading Armadillos' is a wonderfully surprising and trans-formative poem that reaches from cynicism to an improbable and original image of joy. The form is a joy.

My third place poem is centred around three generations who are seated around a dinner table. The scene is familiar enough yet the poem ends up exploring East/West politics, attrition during wartime and its ongoing effects, cultural coding and their potentially destructive ramification as presented through food. The nature imagery is precise in its melodrama yet succinct at revisiting war and how trauma is alert to the smallest indel-icacies. Dinner is not simply dinner, it is an 'Act', a representation of grand narratives; the granddaughter's frustration with chillies in every dish seems to draw the grandmother back to a former conflict as she must try to defend her culture.

My second prize, what we learn from movies about surviving a nuclear blast, dramatizes the terrifying consequences of a nuclear explosion. The witty parallel of an old film with an actual situation that occurred earlier in the year shows desperate nurture and human incapability. The form of the poem, with its teeming line endings and line openings, enact its own anxiety and locks us into the chamber of the language. The poem makes us feel breathless and miasmic as it gathers momentum and brings us into a series of vivid and appalling images. We are reminded that the role of poetry is to provoke, to shock, to warn, and this poem achieves all these terms with deft authority. We are left 'crouched in the cellar or bathroom', as was the case earlier in the year, when Hawaiians were told for 38 minutes that they were under nuclear attack.

My winning poem, 'Exhibition', is a powerful and subtle meditation on sexual dawning and flirtation between the sexes. The speaker is witnessing a scene which reminds them of their own youth and the games of bodily performance and apparent evasion. The speaker is witness to a game of witnessing. The poem increases in complexity as the screw on the syntax is turned and the final sequence is an elongated sentence that offers playfulness yet hints at darker possibilities. Words such as 'pained me' and 'shamelessness' seem to hint at some transgression, but the speaker keeps this narrative out of the poem. A highly accomplished and beautiful poem that's edged between joy and perhaps something foreboding about this watching and being watched.

MONICA ALI

Short Story Report

Reading through this year's entries I thought a lot about what makes a great short story truly great. The best ones make the back of your neck tingle. They make you feel newly alive to the world. They suck you in fast, and they do it by weaving character, setting, story, voice, dialogue and whatever other elements of the craft, into a scene that makes you wonder what will happen next, what has happened before. Many of the less successful stories, though fluently written, relied too heavily on narrative summary, so that the reader was kept at a distance, relying on second hand information instead of watching the story unfold.

The opening of 'Ouroboros' succeeds in raising questions instantly in the reader's mind, creating an immediacy and urgency and desire to delve deeper into the narrator's life. *I was standing in line at a bus stop when I noticed someone had scratched,* all journeys are lies, *on to the lamppost I was leaning on.*

In the brilliant 'Beckett in the Woods' the narrator's grandfather claims to have met Samuel Beckett crawling through the brambles.

When I asked her later why she was so angry about it, my mother refused to say much to me.

'It's all lies,' she said, filling the kettle with a bluster of water. 'It's always been the same with him.'

Appropriately enough for a story about Beckett, many of the questions raised remain unanswered, but we learn a great deal about families.

Families, relationships and marriages formed, not surprisingly, the meat of many of the entries. The best of them, like 'Four Corners', managed to make this well trodden territory fresh. *There were three of us, all girls, all squash players, all undiscovered.*

There was a trend too for use of the present tense. Too often this choice seemed random, adding nothing. Sometimes, as in 'Digging', it was skilfully deployed to build suspense and tension. Or it helped to build character, such as the drug-dealing narrator in 'Near Llandaff', who seems effectively trapped in the present tense.

The stories that stand out are diverse in almost every way but one. They favour the particular over the general. They make the reader see, and therefore *feel*, through the judicious use of precise detail. 'Black Boys' is crammed with such gorgeous particularity. In 'Crossing', when the police enter Gloria's shack, *Their eyes were out for the one-horned goat, the blood-red candles, the black needle cut from a sliver of slave bone.*

Surprisingly few stories touched on the world of social media. One that does so with brio and humour is 'Likes'. Another, written in the form of diary entries, is 'Variation of Molly', which captures so many contemporary anxieties, both cosmically large and comically small.

'Karolina' is a lesson in economy. At only 1,146 words it packs a punch and a twist, and has pathos too. 'Sadness', as with all the best sad stories, is as funny as it is dark. *King said nothing should have that look of sadness in its eyes, not a person nor an animal or even knots in a pine board, but Billgo had it.*

The winning entries are all so fully realized, such true achievements, it seems a shame to rank them in order. 'Wet Bloody Country' is the quietly magnificent tale of a young boy's weekend away with his estranged father in a caravan in Donegal. Told from the child's perspective, it is a lesson in understatement and reading between the lines. The father is brilliantly delineated without judgement ever being directly passed.

On my birthday there was a phone call from Manchester.

'I'm helping them rebuild a football stadium,' he'd said, like the job depended on him alone.

'The Heartsick Diaspora' is innovative in format and original in content. Structured as a play in three acts, along with an opening section titled *Production History/Characters* it is largely written as prose fiction although *Act Two, Scene Two* melds into a script with stage directions. The subject is the tensions within and surrounding an 'ethnic writers group'. It's clever, multi-layered, challenging and political. It's also full of verve and wit.

'Don't use Singlish,' Phoebe says. 'It's pidgin, it makes Western readers laugh at us.'

'The Fore Caddie' is a heartbreaking and beautiful story set in Chennai in the Indian state of Tamil Nadu. The style is deceptively simple, but the mastery of voice and tone and character is anything but simple to achieve. There is a wonderful, delicate balance between humour and poignancy. The author pulls off a stunning feat in this story by imbuing the narrative with both a gorgeous sense of possibility and a deep and disturbing sense of inevitability. The ending is simply another beginning that nevertheless completes the story and makes it achingly whole.

MONICA ALI

Flash Fiction Report

I am in awe of anyone who can write can write decent flash fiction. It's a really tough business to create an entire story, build a world, bring a character to life in so few words. The best of the entries this year left a lingering presence, an impression on the imagination that filled far more space in the mind than on the page. They resonated long after the final line.

In 'Partial', a sweep of family history is encompassed in one single page, five generations linked by a single word. The narrator's grandmother had a partial dental bridge. *A partial bridge can crack, did crack, my mother said. Easily replaced, she said, all you need is money.* These final lines of the opening paragraph, so seemingly innocuous, ring in your ears when you get to the end of the story. Partial remission can't be fixed by money or anything else.

Many of the entries touched on death and loss and packed some emotional heft. Others were touching and also funny. 'Courtship' is a witty, clever and elegant story that weighs in at a mere 98 words. A little miracle of brevity, it conjures a cerebral romance of correspondence, chiefly through the vehicle of a semi-colon.

'Lucky Underpants' describes a romantic encounter that goes awry because the narrator becomes distracted by his own thoughts. One thing definitely leads to another but not to the kind of climax he was originally hoping for. In the space of less than a page we get a sense of character, a sense of the way his mind works. *'Nothing happened,'* says his might-have-been lover, but for the reader plenty has happened, in fact.

Now for the winners, all of them terrific, all perfectly formed.

'What Real Men Wish They Dreamed' makes real use of the title, so important when words are at such a premium. We are dropped into the world of The Miner, driving his buddy to hospital after his hand has been blown off. This guy is tough. But back home, trying to sleep, trying to *tug it to him like a fish on a line*, he wishes to dream of his dead mother, darning a sock that's still on his foot. It's a story about masculinity, what it means to be a 'real man', what's expected, what's hidden and what is yearned for beneath the surface. The story reveals itself sparely, guardedly, the form, character and subject matter in perfect synchronicity.

10

In 'Nan' a granny sits *with prayer beads round her knuckles, her cup cold between her fingers, killing time*. The reader is at once in a fever of suspense. Rightly so, because we soon learn that her grandson is about to be kneecapped and she is to deliver him to the men who will do the deed. It's an agonising situation. She knows there's no escape and she's taken the condemned boy his favourite meal, and *remembered the feathery weight and the smell of him* as a small child. It's perfectly weighted and freighted, the terse lines of dialogue judged perfectly too.

'The Grand Finale' is about the wife of a magician, The Great Fantoni, unpacking his bags when he returns from a world tour. It's a comic tale that is also a kind of magic trick, a perfect marriage of form and content. There is always a danger with flash fiction of everything resting on a final 'punch line', but here that manoeuvre pays off because the ending is built up perfectly, like a magician pulling a rabbit out of a hat.

Congratulations to all the winners and the highly commended entries. I take my hat off also to everyone who entered. The standard was high and making the selections was difficult, but not as difficult as crafting a brilliant piece of fiction in only 250 words.

JOHN FREEMAN

Exhibition

It's a cool afternoon in mid-November.
Boys are messing about beside the river,
and one of them is taking off his shirt.
Perhaps it's for a dare, or someone bet him.
I lose sight of his group among the trees
as I turn and head towards the footbridge,
but it sounds as if he must be in by now.
A dozen girls in brand-new uniforms
crowd along the path in my direction.
I notice how, whatever the colour
and the thickness of their hair, all of them
have it pulled tightly back above their foreheads.
Once you focus on it, it's a motif,
the smooth brow and the lines of hair above it.
They must be eleven, twelve at most.
Though I've lost sight of the bare-chested boy,
the girls haven't. They're pretending not to look,
not to be impressed or interested.
One of them, with dark curls, her lowered face
suffused with a becoming rosiness,
gives an involuntary, inward smile.
Who knows what is going on inside her?
I'm remembering when I was her age,
or thereabouts, and the smooth-skinned boy's,
seeing an older lad at a French resort
with a friend, no doubt egging him on,
facing a sand-dune, changing to swim, naked,
with narrow hips, flexing his small, hard buttocks,
smirking, glancing further up the beach
to where two girls, in their midteens as he was,
demurely dressed, holding down pleated skirts,
were sitting on a wall, giggling together,

one of them leaning back in the direction
of the sea to look past the dunes, almost
toppling, to glimpse perhaps the first male nude –
it was a different world – she'd met with, and I
didn't know which surprised and pained me more,
his shamelessness, or the girl's fascination.

LUISA A. IGLORIA

what we learn from movies about surviving a nuclear blast

8:09 01 13 18 Ballistic Missile Threat inbound to Hawai'i

early in the film I a bright orange cloud I dust-colored horizon of a little town I with fake storefronts & fake people I such a charming test site I they have everything I down to the last detail I naugahyde couch & anti-macassar I chintz curtains I the father mother & children I facing the television I watching not watching the news I they really don't have I any idea what's coming I except for the hero who's stumbled onto the set I there's no voice coming over the intercom I saying *seek immediate shelter this is not a drill please remain I calm & follow instructions* I the hero makes a beeline for the refrigerator I tossing out shelves & bins I the carton of milk I the eggs & onions I it's a new model with sea-foam green interiors I fully lined with lead I he climbs in just in the nick of time I the expanding saturn rings from the blast I torch everything I that can't duck & cover I or clamber into a fallout shelter I its sign three inverted yellow triangles I deadly trefoil mushrooming I within a circle of black I just a few weeks ago I i noticed for the first time a sign like that I half-faded on the brick wall of a local high school I in that movie it's 1957 & the hero survives I but the others turn sort of incandescent I you can see their entire skeleton I all 206 bones lit up I a fiery x-ray meaning the flesh I has melted is melting or is gone I what do you think they did I in hawai'i that day I for 38 minutes I crouched in the cellar or bathroom I covering their children's bodies I with their own

ASHISH XIANGYI KUMAR

The Act of Dinner

If the food's not finished
my mother sits there watching it.
She will eat it, all of it, as her face
moves over the table like a searchlight
going out into foggy sea.

My daughter sometimes says,
It's not the Japanese occupation!
and then laughs in a way
that splits an iceberg very far away.

My mother's face is a fist of desperate
deliberation. She will always say,
I like to eat, I like food.
She's careful to laugh too, and puts
chili padi[1] in everything she cooks.
Her fork moves minutely. She erodes
a bank of rice into a thin sliver, watching
her life sort itself out. Where she lives

there is no danger, her blouse is crisp,
water might move this way and that
but is harmless. But today my daughter twists
her vegetables into a knot, asks,
Must you put chilli in everything?

and when my mother looks up at her
she is struck dumb as a lighthouse
looking out to land: for in her mind
it is impossible to imagine
that this, too, is a weapon.

1 Bird's-eye chilli.

PATRICIA CANTWELL

Atonement

When I asked what they did with them – the miscarriages –
The young doctor shrugged her shoulders and said
'I don't know, I think they burn them'.

My aunt gave me a rug-making kit.
Said it would give me something to do
And keep my mind off things.
Eight red roses on a black background.
The size of a small grave.

Each day I laid it on the long table
And pulled the coarse wool through the thick canvas
With a crochet hook until my fingers bled.
The ravelled petals like open wounds resisted stitching.
Not being a natural needlewoman I never got the hang of it.
My father said I was a great beginner but never finished anything.

And so it lay abandoned in the attic with the Christmas decorations
Until finally we put it on the bonfire one November night
And watched the eight red roses bleed upward in the winter sky.

EMILY CHEN

Mirror, Mirror, On the Wall

I like to think every self-respecting Chinese queer
    has written poetry about their mother
and the bruise that bloomed aster when they told her
    they were gay, they were villains, they were
going to be Buffy the Vampire Slayer for Halloween.
    I imagine every self-respecting Chinese queer
has slipped in the word *mother* near *knife* or *lonely*
    or *beautiful*, but never *love* without *not*.
This is a poem about a mother, only the mother
    does not know. The mother does not know
her daughter is only Olympic in dysmorphics,
    that her daughter does not want her in the bathroom
when she is undressed. We could be twins, our bodies
    pale and pear-like beneath the fluorescent stage lights.
We could be twins, only she has borne two children,
    and her skin still drips near the belly, and the still-dark stain
stretches into seventeen years. The bathroom box is
    small and open. Condensation cures us of our fears
of being seen, as though our hearts are make-believe.
    You can't come in when I'm naked, I say. The mother does not know
why her daughter is rejecting her. Maybe she has a tattoo – or a child.
    Maybe she is every self-respecting Chinese queer and is afraid
of the –man who will touch where only she and the mirror have seen.
    You are disrespecting me, I say. The mother does not know,
and she is silent. Privacy is a commodity she had learned to forgo,
    for the price of a man between her legs had never been worth
the prize of a lonely bed. Mothers and loneliness and daughters
    who will not speak. Daughters who have lost their mothers' self-respect.
The bathroom door creaks, and the distance closes in clenched steps.
    I am your mother, she says, and a light bulb tapers out.

HEATHER DERR-SMITH

Memory *(Potacari)*

I told you about the video of the men in Srebrenica being led
to their execution, but you already knew it by heart. The birds sang, new
green buds on the branches of the trees in the woods, and the living fell dead

into the fresh sprung grass. It's morning now in a new century and the dew
pearls on the petals of the wild roses tangled along the road
retracing their footsteps together, climbing to the village, where only a few

houses remain, sundered by shells and blackened with soot, mold
growing up the walls of the empty rooms, blots of mildew, bowed
shoulders of the missing, in their horrible stillness. Astounded by loss,

we follow the winding path they once trod through stecci and ruins,
smell of sweet clover and the charred trunks of trees, call of feral cats
in the moss on the old stones of the mosque. How everything is

connected here, joint to joint, how everything is bound together.
The sun burns away the mist. In the valley a wolf harries
his own shadow. Another world lopes toward us or beyond us,
dark hooves of the horses marking the trail in the birch copse

and we count down to some kind of reckoning, still counting the corpses
to reach one cross-haired, cross-sighted end-point. We bow our heads to death.
The fire gives birth to flame, and the flame is smoke and the smoke is earth.

MELISSA GOODBOURN

Cliff Top Trail

I spot
      the tuft of grass
            think, *this is the one*
at the edge of a path
      marked dangerous cliffs

yet I have
      only known it
            to be dangerous once –
the winter we had 7-foot drifts
      and arctic winds

when sledges
      blew backwards
            up the hills, and if
I was to end it, I would end it here –
      an orange night

the seaweed air,
      the echo
            of kittiwakes
against the cliff, boats swarmed
      and docked

the harbour lined
      with lobster pots,
            stones still circling
the cove
      and you waiting

for me to return
      the way watercress
            waits to grow
from wool and seed,
      a breeze

catches my scarf
      and I think how often
          we lean into
gale-force winds
      hoping not to fall.

VANESSA LAMPERT

Curations

The day comes late summer – you hear the ratchet clicks
of the police car's handbrake beyond the kitchen window.
The two officers walk up the path too fast, to tell you that
your son is dead. The woman assumes intimacy, her hand heavy,
awkward on your arm. You can smell milk
on her breath. You'll remember always the sheen
on the fabric of her jacket. The thought of her hovers;
how she must be moving through the minutes of her day
in the evening telling her husband of the *boy, only 25*
who took enough pills to kill a racehorse. That's what
he typed in. You see the cut potato on her fork, the lift
to her open mouth, the jut of her chin to meet it.
They walk from the house with their dog, her knowing
everything she could have done was gathered up, curated.
And September's here, you can feel it playing with your hair.

JENNI MAZARAKI

In Japan

I caught the wrong bus and before long was waiting to be picked up by my host
family my Okaasan was fuming silent through the glass I saw it all before she even
pulled up to the curb with me standing so tall that I felt like a tree that was waiting to
be climbed or cut down I couldn't tell which when I got in the car she would not look
at me not even in the reflection of the rear view mirror in the backseat I sat with my
legs tucked up neatly knees together my breath quiet so I did not offend the drive was
a quiet one my host sister sat in front and I admired the way that she could sit with her
mother's silence without care at home in my room I put on my headphones then
helped to set the table for dinner and then I went up to my host brother and asked him
for a smoke he was twenty and I was fifteen and he said no.

KEVIN McCARTHY

Now and Then

Dusky dome spilling lowdermilk,
wind-textured laughter wheeling

Ripe mosaic halos and poised
arms of light

      Organs in the territory belonging

I could gather this scent of warm pine,
with bright pledge of hollow moon –
sticky clean and deep

Paint the contours of your body,
and my hands would finish
in black silver

      Still everything and nothing remains

Ducking through blooming trees,
you arrive with two small flowers
in your hair and a ladybug
          on your shoulder

SIMON MIDDLETON

Space was a material

Next time we see him, he is a still-life
arranged in a plastic box.

A Special Care Nurse leads us to an incubator
like a guide at a museum, where we stand
at excruciating distance

surveying a diorama beyond Perspex
examining the thin rise and fall of his back.

We stand as we did once
whilst visiting Hepworth's studio
natural light alive against whitewash walls

our focus centred on a table
with a plinth that held
the polished form of an '*Infant*'.

Remember how little air there was?
How the whole fabric of our lives seemed to fray
and re-thread, so the room felt pliant somehow?

And how, standing before '*Three Forms*'
we were told, *For Hepworth, space was a material*
distance a quality – as much a part of the composition.

In the ward, machines draw his life on a screen
in shallow peaks, as he lies beneath a knitted sheet.

Remember how little air there was in Hepworth's room?
Seeing the child she shaped, knowing ours
was firing in the kiln of your womb.

Was it then we first knew the texture of longing?
Or is that now? Seeing the half-strapped face, the ventilator trunk

the scalp crowned with gingering blood
the newness of a body mapped by wires.

Remember how the air seemed to cement, suddenly?
As we found our hands parting a break in the air

venturing a terrified palm inside
to trace the frightening space above his tiny form

afraid to cup a part of it
in fear we may dent the fontanelles
disrupt the shallow concertina of his lungs.

Is this where we are now?
Wheeling you through the world's corridors
knowing you're safe in a tank, with the outside kept out.

Placed in untenable spaces, feeling the material
of our lives tighten, compress to rigid shape

barely breathing with the strain.

The Dorset Prize is given annually to the writer from Dorset placed highest in the competition. It is generously sponsored by The Bookshop, Bridport, the town's independent book store.

MARK PAFFARD

Burial Chambers

I say 'cromlech', just to myself,
as we sup our fine brown pints
like people of an old religion,
the screen zonking from Snoop-Dogg to Abba,
but nothing much doing tonight.
Ask our landlady, dry as tinder,
allowing the boys at the end to josh
two women on double vodkas.
There's no spark, she needs a fag,
and no-one is kissed and sleep is far off.

The cromlech is a mote on the map
in one of its folds, not North or South
and Google has forgotten it.
We find it by the pout of our lips
when we say it: 'cromlech, crOMlech',
and the muddy hiss in our ears.

And here it is, still standing somehow,
looking down a long green ruck
to Newhaven, while Preseli
boils with cloud: Pentre Ifan,
probably shorn of its outer walls
by needy hands of the later dead
to leave a sixteen ton, five metre,
granite capstone, almost afloat.

For all its lovely Welsh humour
the pub tonight is too open to the winds.
We stay within our thick stone walls
and soon you snore gently – *cromlech, cromlech* –
with your memories like the slain
attendants they dig up in these places
and lean against me like the landscape
twining with bone in our afterlife.

SAM PHIPPS

Reversal

my father was no
violent man
but his backhanders
would surprise you

sometimes from
the driver's seat he'd
twist half blind
to stun your face

some of the shame
you felt at once
creep through your tears
for his disgrace

ALISON THOMPSON

Trading Armadillos

By fifty he'd traded it all: the car, the wife, the house;
  the only thing left to be rid of
    was his heart.

In the park a woman said, I'll trade you an armadillo, so
they swapped, and he settled the armadillo deep within his chest
    where it fitted neatly, seemed the right weight.

He felt pride in its vigor, rejoiced
  at the new strength lying within him but soon
    he became restless, he began to feel endangered,
      found himself suffocating. As the pain in his chest rose
        he wondered how his heart had survived in the outside world?
      Had it formed a protective shell – or a tongue to eat worms?
      And as the armadillo clawed its way free the dying man
  looked up and saw that his heart had sprouted wings
and was perched in a tree, tremulously beating,
        singing its freedom softly
        like a cautious bird.

V. SANJAY KUMAR

The Fore Caddie

'Will you ever buy a house?' asked his friend Mano.

Yuva saw stars. 'No,' he said.

'There is one for sale; cheap. My neighbour, the driver, needs money for an operation.'

Yuva thought about it. 'How much? Actually don't tell me. I might kill someone. Or sell a kidney.'

'Nobody will buy your kidney,' said Mano.

'We will see. How much?'

'Ten lacs. Cash. It has a toilet.'

A private toilet was worth something. 'I don't have the money,' said Yuva. 'I have never seen ten lac rupees in my life.'

'Why don't you rob a bank?' said Mano.

Yuva thought about it. There was a big bank next to jewellery stores. People came in Mercedes cars and bought diamond necklaces for 2-3 lacs. Cash. Every day the stores sent sacks full of notes to the Bank Branch. Yuva imagined the heist. The guard would be seated outside the bank branch with his big antique rifle. There would be a few customers, old men and women who still visited the bank. And some middle-class wimps who served as bank officers. All Mano and Yuva had to do was wear masks, knock the guard down, and threaten people. Nobody inside would be brave enough to resist.

His stomach made a noise. When things were really quiet Yuva could hear it. It had a mind of its own and near the McRennett's pastry shop it growled. The smell of fresh baking came through the door. His insides contracted. A man walked past carrying hot buns in a brown paper bag, the butter stains showing.

'Go in first,' he told Mano. 'I will follow.'

He walked in behind him. The place was cool and the smell was heavenly. Yuva asked the salesgirl the price of a few items. He pretended he couldn't make up his mind. Mano hated this charade. He pulled at Yuva's sleeve. 'Let's go, machan,' he said. The salesgirl smiled at Yuva.

30

She reached into the counter, pulled out a fresh cream pastry, and offered it to him. 'Take it,' she said. It was soft and it had a white creamy layer on which were two juicy pieces of pineapple and one red cherry. His stomach lurched as he held it. Outside he took a big bite and gave the rest to his friend. The fresh cream melted in his mouth. The pineapple had been dipped in sugar syrup. He licked his lips.

How did she know? How did she guess he had no money? Was it obvious?

'She likes me,' he told Mano.

'Machan,' said Mano, 'you look hungry.'

'She felt sorry for me?'

'Yes,' said Mano. 'You are lucky you look hungry.'

He felt hungry all the time. His mother said it was because he was growing. He knew it wasn't just about food.

The first time they stole it was a packet of chips from a store. Yuva refused to open it. The next day he wanted to return it. 'Don't,' said Mano. A day later the packet was still there. They ripped it open and ate the chips, one by one. 'You shouldn't think so much,' said Mano. Yuva stopped thinking. He flicked pencils and pens in the Corporation school. He left his old slippers outside a temple and wore someone else's. He stole savouries as he walked past street vendors and burnt his fingers once. A couple of times he had to run. He was fast and he knew the city well. Once he ducked into a house while being chased and in a split second he straightened, walked slowly up to the door, picked up a milk packet from the floor, bit its corner, drank it, and left.

'We have to stop looking like rowdies,' said Mano. 'Otherwise we will get caught. The police will take one look at us and put us in the locker.'

'How?' asked Yuva. 'Should we steal some clothes?'

'Look at yourself,' said Mano. They stood beside a car, bent, and looked at themselves in the side mirror.

'What's wrong?'

'Your face is pinched, your cheeks are hollow, and your eyes.'

'What about my eyes?'

'You look like you just ran away from a Home.'

Yuva used his fingers to brush and flatten his hair. He widened his eyes and stuck his tongue out. 'What should we do?'

'Eat properly for ten days. Our look will improve.'

A week later they went to a pavement shop, the kind that popped up unexpectedly and shut before the constabulary arrived. The vendor spread his wares, set up a board that declared a cut price and a crowd gathered in no time. Yuva picked up a showy shirt. 'No,' said Mano.

'Not that belt,' said his friend. Yuva put back the shiny belt.

'Here, wear these glasses.' They had clear lenses. 'Glasses make you look honest,' said Mano.

'Why?'

'Because thieves don't wear spectacles.'

That evening they wore their new clothes and went mad.

'Gana, gana, gana,' shouted Mano, shaking his hips. He was twisting into a rope, and he was leaping the length of the room. The Tamil song was on speaker and it went thud, thud, thud. 'Yuvan Shankar Raja,' said Mano, shouting out the name of their favourite music composer. Yuva got started. He could dance. Parts of his body that did nothing for a week came alive. He shifted from toe to toe and soon his hands were moving, his eyes slanted, his knee bent stylishly.

'Thalaiva,' shouted Mano, 'what a pose!'

Yuva pumped his shoulders, fluidly skated to the wall, and halted. 'Dai Michael,' he yelled, turned once, twice, and twirled the hat on his head. Thump, thump, thump.

'Go, go, go,' said his friend.

They had been drinking. Yuva danced harder, beating himself with his hands, throwing his head from side to side. He saw stars. The music kept playing and he couldn't stop. He was sweating profusely and he felt thirsty. He drank more beer. The angels came, soft, white, and fluffy. They settled into his arms. 'Machan, can you see them?' he said. The song slowed, the beat petered out. A ballad began to a slow rhythm. His horny friend hugged him, thrusting his bony hips into Yuva's back. They fell on their backs, exhausted.

*

Yuva remembered his first possessions. His first golf ball had no maker's name because it had been erased by use. It was egg-shell white many months ago, now its colour was mud. His first golf club was a broken five iron that he had repaired. Its grip was hard and his fingers had blisters for a month.

The Gymkhana was his home course. He had grown up in it as a fore caddie. During practice sessions players stood in a line and teed off, shouting fore. Yuva and his young friends ran holding their heads, picked up the balls and placed them in buckets. He liked going on rounds as a fore caddie. The Gymkhana was a links course with evil rough; tall unkempt grass where balls could easily get lost. Yuva stood a hundred yards ahead of the players and tracked where the ball went. Golfers employed a fore caddie because the cost was lower than the cost of a new golf ball. A lost ball also meant a penalty and on occasion a penalty meant a lost bet.

Yuva started at the age of five. He ran fast during practice and kept his eyes peeled. If a ball went missing he got cuffed behind the ear by the caddie master. Those days he had one proper pair of shorts tied to his waist by a thin rope. He had a T-shirt that was big for him. All his shirts were bigger than him till he was in his teens. They wore sponsor logos and were made of synthetic material. They were hand me downs from players.

Some afternoons, in summer, the course was empty and no one was around to stop him and his three friends from entering the place. They carried a club each and some old balls. He had his trusty five iron. He played the entire course with one club, putting with it as well. He learnt the game without caring for style or technique. He had an athletic free-flowing swing. His ball flight was long and he could chip the ball in ten different ways. He learnt how to read greens. The big slope and the small slopes. The grain of the grass. The way it had been cut.

His father was a senior caddie. He would mimic the players he had caddied for. He would mimic their English. 'Golf teaches you how to be honest,' he said, with a straight face. He would laugh uproariously and then very solemnly he would say in Tamil. 'But God teaches you how to make a living.'

Yuva learnt to help players out. He learnt how to improve the lie of the ball so that it could be hit better. He could do this with his feet. His toes curled around the ball and moved it. He would place the ball on a tuft of grass or a patch of upraised soil. In the tall grass called rough he learnt how to shift the ball into shorter grass. He would pretend to be searching even after finding the ball. He would place the ball where it could be hit easily, move away, then come back and shout as if he had just found it. He learnt to walk with the ball in his toes. He walked many a yard with it and old players began to brag about how long they were hitting the ball. With him as caddie the members scored better. He received fat tips.

His mother was extremely unhappy when he followed his father to the golf course. She shouted at both of them.

'Don't you have any dreams?' she asked Yuva.

'Only dreams,' he said.

He was so young nothing could be better than going with his old man to this huge open playground where he could run around on green grass with his friends, and occasionally play a game for free.

'Your son will become a jobless drunk, like you,' shouted his mother, at Old Man. Old Man stood in the doorway, his cap in his hand, his teeth showing. He had a wicked grin. He was past caring about anything, least of all his son. His wife hated it that he was on retainer because it made him lazy and he carried the bag just three times a week and refused to do so on other days. She hated that he got a lump sum every month because he ran out of money in the middle and ate into her earnings.

'Go and stand in line with the rest of them every morning and carry the bag.'

'No,' he said. 'I am tired of running after cars, tired of bribing the caddie master, and bloody tired of fighting for tips.'

'Why? You think you are superior to the rest? Know your place. You are a daily wage earner. You have no pension. I won't be around to take care of you when your liver says get lost.'

*

Old Man was caddie for Big Man. Big Man was an addict who spent big money on golf. He bought a home in the hills in Kodaikanal next to the golf course. He travelled to exotic locations to scenic courses with his friends. He bought the latest clubs when they hit the market. And he engaged the best coaches to improve his game. Big Man was a poor player, a hacker, who moved heaven and mostly earth in his earnest attempts to be a good golfer. Large chunks of soil got thrown about when he played and after he finished a round in Kodaikanal it seemed the bison had invaded the course again and left their hoofmarks in the fairways.

He played thrice a week, alone if he had to. Single ball, it was called. A bird, a view of the setting sun, a tree in bloom, soft grass under his feet, a cross breeze, a dog at rest in a sand bunker; these were things that evoked feelings in him. Was nature the only reason he spent five hours sweating and burning up in the heat that Chennai produced every day?

'It is a game of half-truths,' he said, when asked. 'I feel this is what brings people in and keeps them hooked.'

The whole truth, like a tournament prize, eluded him.

'You chase a small ball through hill and dale, rough and fairway, sand and grass, over water, under trees. You shape your shots, sometimes inadvertently.' He remembered fondly a high fade over branches onto a hidden flag. How could he forget that sudden low draw around a tree that hit the flag and went into the hole?

'You are called an amateur because that is an honourable status, not a comment on your ability,' said his uncle. 'The correct term for you is hacker.' His uncle was a good player, a scratch golfer in his heyday, and a stickler for rules.

Big Man was hurt. He joined a gym and worked on his core, hoping it would improve his game. The hacking continued.

'It is a mental game,' said his uncle.

Old golfers like his uncle were a pain. They were full of pithy statements and horny jokes. They were rule bound, waiting to pounce on newcomers who hadn't memorized the Royal and Ancient's bible.

'We are a necessary curse,' said his uncle, 'because most newcomers are illiterate and uncouth.'

Big Man tolerated his uncle because the latter had helped in getting a membership. He remembered standing in the bar waiting for his admission interview. He was wearing a suit. The trousers were tight because he sat on his arse longer than he should have. He was nervous. He wasn't sure he had survived the test round. Despite having played the game for many months he could not play a round of 18 or under. His uncle had played with him on his test round and marked his card.

'Years of study have done me no good,' he told his uncle, after the round. 'I have studied the game. I have studied my swing. And I have learnt the rules.'

'And?'

'Truth is life sucks.'

His honesty struck a chord. There could be no other reason for his uncle giving him a leg up in the Committee meeting.

*

Yuva grew into his old man's sandals, became a full caddie, got a retainer from Big Man, and most evenings he drank himself into a stupor.

'The cheapest liquor is the best. I don't care how it is packed, what the bottle looks like, how it is poured and whether I am seated or standing. Usually I am standing.'

It was a busy place, there were two-wheelers and cycles, people wearing helmets, the road smelling of piss. There was a concrete counter and booze was slapped down on it, money appearing from inside shorts which were inside veshtis, the notes grubby and wet. The shopkeeper was old and behaved like he was doing Yuva a favour.

'I am a regular and he does not recognize me.'

A half cut lemon turned its face, its two eyes were seeds. Salt was on the counter, a little wet, still good enough. Nearby was the sound of frying. Potatoes, banana fritters, aubergine slices, tomatoes. Red-brown coated, carrying the latest headline from the newspaper they were served in. Everybody was smoking. The labourers smoked unfiltered beedis, the office-goers smoked cigarettes.

'What happened to your father?' asked the shopkeeper, out of the blue.

'He died,' said Yuva, startled that the shopkeeper knew who he was all along.

Old Man had a large and forgiving liver that soaked the booze and his kidneys worked overtime and they chugged along for three decades till one small ulcer built up, gradually, into an abscess. The day it burst the bleed could not be stemmed. Nobody was around to help him as his wife was woman enough to have dumped him. Old Man called Yuva and by the time he arrived his father had croaked. He left nothing behind by way of money or possessions. Whatever was of value was inside a safe in a pawnbroker's shop. Yuva went there looking to retrieve the stuff but was chased away.

*

Yuva was at his worst behaviour on the days Big Man did not play. Like his father he refused to stand in line with the daily wage earners and carry the bag for someone else. Daily wage business was stressful. Some days you got stuck with badly behaved golfers who cursed the caddie for every mishap. Some days you were allotted the misers that most caddies avoided. Some days you rushed with the others to every car that came and others got chosen. Each time you returned to the group you either cursed or pretended to be crestfallen so others could laugh. Yuva and Manu, the ones with monthly retainers, would arrive just to watch. They would chat with the rest, crack some jokes, and while away the morning.

Early afternoon was booze time. There would be standing space next to a six feet by six feet opening in the wall. A board hung by a nail and a couple of letters had erased themselves. What remained was ASMA BAR. T and C were missing from TASMAC.

'I should be going to college,' said Yuva.

'Me too,' said Mano.

Both feet were on the ground, left knee was slightly bent. Yuva was holding the bottle and it was half empty. Half of it was spoken for, the other half they would argue with through the day till it won them over.

'Bloody flirt this alcohol,' said Mano, slurring slightly.

'Cannot finish it before noon.'

'I know, I know.'

They had been warned. This was the road to early death, lined by livers, blood in their trousers when they peed, blood in their eyes when they woke up. Yuva kept the bottle in an inside pocket in his pant and his loose shirt hung past his hips.

'Nobody can see it.'

It had a simple shape and a screw cap. Yuva could open it with one hand. They drank it straight, from the bottle. They liked to feel the spirit go down their throat, warm, on a good day some bite, and sometimes some taste.

'I don't like the taste. I don't know why they add it.'

'My piss smells. Sometimes my sweat smells. I don't know why they add smell.'

The days Big Man showed up life was whole. Yuva would be sober, his hair combed. Like his father did before him he would be philosophic, watching the hacking. Golf was a hard game especially for those who lacked aptitude. There really was no one to blame after a while.

'Shoulder drop, Master,' said Yuva, when he couldn't take it anymore.

Big Man broke a club occasionally.

'Chinese clubs, Master,' said Yuva, holding the splintered shaft. 'Cheap, but not good.'

Balls got lost in the rough ever so often.

'Committee making course difficult, Master,' said Yuva.

He did his bit, helping out, moving the ball ahead with his feet, improving the lie. Big Man became moody as he aged. Some days he shouted. Some days he was generous, uncontrollably happy when he made a long putt or hit his tee shot onto the green on a par three.

'His knees are giving him trouble,' said Yuva.

Mano shrugged. 'So?'

'I can see him struggle to bend and pick up the ball from the hole. Sometimes he struggles to bend and tee up the ball but he insists on doing it himself.'

The weather was bloody in the summer, the sun naked like a flame. The heat rose from the ground, scorching the grass, or what was left of it. The course was near the sea and there was salt in the air. Twelve months a year it was humid and muggy. At the end of a five hour golf round everybody was tired, thirsty, and happy it was over.

'He is not my boss,' said Yuva. 'I can walk away.'

Mano laughed. 'Does he even notice you?'

'Sometimes we look at each other. He wants me to smile. He has never seen me laugh. He wants to. Sometimes he tips me heavily, while looking at me.'

'And?'

'Thanks Master, I say coolly. That's it. I take it and walk away.'

'Does he like you?'

'Yes. He tells me all kinds of private things. He was very fond of my father. He remembers him very often.'

'He wasn't there at your father's cremation,' said Mano.

A crisis was around the corner. There was a dark golf round waiting to happen, a terrible day on the course when nothing would work, when the accumulated frustration of Big Man would turn on Yuva as the reason for it all. Change of caddie would be the last solution.

It was a tournament when the sordid deed happened. And Big Man was playing with his uncle in the four ball, and playing badly. After nine holes of watching the torture his uncle spoke up. 'This game is not idiot proof,' he said. 'There are fourteen ways to make a fool of yourself because there are fourteen clubs in your bag. On a bad day fourteen snakes.'

The smallest club had an open face and it was spiteful. It was called sand wedge. Big Man had just fifteen feet to the flag and there was a sand bunker in between. All he had to do was accelerate through the stroke like Yuva had told him a million times. He stabbed at the ball and it plopped into the sand, cosied itself inside and only half was visible.

'Fried egg,' said his uncle, almost rubbing his hands, imagining what would come next.

The next shot flew low over the green and into the deep rough beyond. Yuva ran to find the ball. And then he turned away unable to look at what followed. Big Man should have taken a penalty and a drop but he did not because he had to show his uncle he could play his way out of the rough. He hacked the grass twice and the ball went in deeper each time. They couldn't see it now. Clumps of grass were strewn around and some grass was on his hat and his clothes. Yuva looked away. 'Master?' he said.

Big Man took the sand wedge and hit a bench, once, twice. The wedge broke.

'I think you just killed a snake,' said his uncle.

At the bar after things had cooled off his uncle had some advice for his nephew. 'Change your caddie,' he said. 'Sometimes it helps. Don't ask me why.'

And so it happened, just like that, for no reason at all. The abruptness was hateful, the lack of discernible reason hurt Yuva more than anything else. Yuva stayed home. Mano took his place on the course.

After a few days Yuva joined the daily wage line, forcing himself to run up to the cars that came by. When Big Man's car showed up he had to hide.

'Just do your job well and people will respect you,' his mother said. She said that to make him feel better but he felt worse because he knew that as a day caddie he couldn't earn it. There were too many of them available, eager to bear with everything that the players threw at them, eager to cheat on their behalf. Respect was a rag that had been torn to bits, dragged by the foot into a daily wage hole that had them by the balls.

The next day he had no assignment. Yuva walked purposefully towards the practice range. The Caddie Master and part-time coach saw him approach.

'What are you doing here?'

Yuva ignored him. He picked up a bucket and walked a hundred yards towards the gaggle of young boys running around picking up balls. The boys saw him approach and began giggling. He stood amongst them, tall, and out of place.

Fore, shouted one of the players. A ball described an arc, soaring towards the blue sky. Yuva needed no urging. He stumbled in his hurry and fell. He picked himself up and he ran.

ELAINE CHIEW

The Heartsick Diaspora

i. Production History/Characters

Our ethnic writers group that used to meet weekly at a Cafe Nero in Bayswater upgraded itself to a Le Pain Quotidien in Notting Hill. Kevan (often mispronounced as Kevin) is our de facto leader because he takes care of all email distributions with a rather dictatorial leadership style, but has such spiky long lashes, everyone else in the group, who is female, forgives him. He's also an eccentric because he has us writing in strange places e.g. on a bus, while queuing at the post office, and once, at a chippie. To court our ethnically-inclined muses, he says. We've written while holding contorted yoga positions or photographing bicycle racks and empty car-parks with cars bisected half-in half-out of the frame (hide-and-seek car, as titled). Once, at an art exhibit where one of the artists had an obsession for tiny animal penises as an investigation into male impotence. None of us could identify which animals were being featured – the photographs were very abstract.

There is Miranda, our 'yogi' with her intermittent mantra-chantings, her downward dogs, her occasional dabble into tarot card readings, and her immediate jump to alertness whenever anyone mentions their remembered dreams or personal psychological revelation. She's Malaysian Chinese and she's writing a story about an old woman with urinary incontinence, but can't seem to make up her mind whether the old woman is Chinese from the old country – THE MOTHERLAND – Miranda even says this in a booming voice to emphasise, or whether the old woman ought to be Malaysian Chinese. Makes a difference, she says.

Well, not in Britain, it does not (mutters Phoebe, who is Singaporean Chinese, hence 'causeway' rivalry, like Britain and France). Phoebe is the kind of touchy-feely who touches the inside of your wrist and it feels like a poke, the outside of your elbow, and it feels like a jab. She has a four-year old daughter, and she's writing a story about an Asian mother who raps when she's upset. Little does she know that the young mother in Miranda's story is really Phoebe, and the four-year-old girl in the story is Phoebe's precious drama queen, Priscilla (whom we secretly nickname

'Prissy' because she can't stomach a single speck of dirt on her Mary Janes). Phoebe on a typical day as she peers into your eyes: 'May I ask how your project is going? Are you feeling momentum?' She unloads harsh critique on an ill-written story like a case of stormy weather.

Miranda, bless her heart, has devised a code word for those of us on the receiving end of one of Phoebe's blitzkrieg – MARLIN – as in Hemingway's *Old Man and The Sea*, when the marlin is devoured by sharks and the old fisherman there is sinking into depression. MARLIN is an effective intervention protocol: a hastily-gathered band of us converges upon the afflicted with chicken soup, Jewish bagels or an array of baked goods to restore his/her 'soul'. Miranda has an atavistic faith in the restorative powers of baked goods.

Finally, there's me. Chandra. I tick all the people-on-the-fringe boxes – female who dresses up quite androgynous, ambidextrous, biracial (half Indian, half Chinese) – everything about me is ambiguous. My writing is frequently populated by people so quirky and weird that maybe they shouldn't exist. We're all frauds of one kind or another, located here in this time and place. Miranda and Phoebe think I vacillate between extremes of emotion and personality. Either I'm too militant – why does everything need to be so political, your Facebook posts are so peppered with denunciations of 'isms – or I'm too cynical. And I think they're either sickeningly adorable or annoyingly peevish. Still, as one fraud might say to another (apt considering British weather), *you've got too many layers on.*

ii. Act One Scene One
Was it Tolstoy who said: All stories begin with someone coming to town or someone leaving town? Well, at one of our weekly gatherings, Kevan announces we may have a new cell member. We're a MeetUp group that ended up bonding. We separated out of a larger cluster, like a reproducing amoeba. While it was never stated or agreed that we wouldn't include anyone else, we also realised we had good group dynamics, spiced up just enough by the rivalry between Phoebe and Miranda. And to be honest, I think Kevan rather enjoys his 'harem' of Asian women.

His name is Wei. Wei looks like a Korean *hallyu* flower-boy – double eyelids, long lashes, feminine lips, high cheek-bones, six-foot sporting a six-pack. He slings ramen as a line cook at Wagamama, and wafts the scent of pork bones and spring onions. He toddles up on a crisp spring morning, the daffodils have just come out in Hyde Park, and I fell in love. Instant, crushing, overpowering jolt of emotion, straight to the solar plexus. Such a clean shot, it actually hurts.

Wei sits down next to me and all my pores open up. Even the hair on my arms wave their tendril heads.

By way of introduction, Kevan tells Wei that all four of us were glorious once, receiving prizes and accolades for our writing and whatnot. A logroll of our prizes and accolades would include being named Thirty Under Thirty by the prestigious LitFly (one of only two minorities on the list), winning a FOMO (Fiction of Minority Origin) Award, numerous short-listings in numerous 'lucrative' and not-so-lucrative literary prizes started by coffee shops et. al, and finally, one of us won the trophy in a gameshow called Pig in a Poke where no pokes were involved and no animals were harmed (the whatnot bit – Kevan).

Wei throws us all a laddish smile – a little bad-ass, a little conspiratorial, and managing to be mega-watt at the same time (how does one even do that, emotionally multi-task like that?) Kevan asks us to tell Wei what we're working on. Phoebe lies through her teeth, says she's working on some story set-up like David Henry Hwang's play *Yellow Face*. Pretentious git. In her story, an ABC (American-born Chinese) hires a Frenchman to pose as the executive chef of her French restaurant because Asian people can't cook French gourmet but they can sure write sci-fi. Lie or not, the plot sounds impressive, if she can carry it off.

Miranda opens with an 'amituo-fo' (greetings from the Buddha? strange woman!), and laughs, employing all her teeth (molars, even her dangly uvula, quivering like a tiny penis – muse put to good use). Miranda tells the story of an old woman who remembers a particular episode involving Ben-wa balls inserted into her vagina as she rides pillion on a bicycle; Wei's eyes open wide; Phoebe clamps down her teeth.

It's Kevan's turn. None of us knows what Kevan is really working on. We suspect he isn't really writing anything, haven't been for a while. A Marlin is due. He says, the group is meant to be supportive. We pride ourselves on this. But you also have to learn to withstand pain. Occasionally, in spite of the hail of criticisms, a glimmer of admiration will seep through in someone's remarks, and that's what we live for – that despite all the flaws in our work, sometimes we manage to surprise ourselves.

Wei nods. Like Phoebe, he's also working on a story that incorporates food. His protagonist is a young man who gets haunted by a hungry ghost with a confused identity – she can't decide whether she's a Malay *pontianak* or a Chinese *èguǐ* (customary hungry ghost). The former only drinks blood; the latter eats *kim zua* (joss paper products the Chinese burn for their dead.)

Oh my god, I won't be able to refrain from planting my chops where they don't belong.

Phoebe's mouth dangles half-open. Then she adjusts the perpetual sunglasses perched on top of her head and pats Wei on the arm. 'You know that Chinese people love proverbs, right? Great minds think alike. Birds of a feather flock together. Three unskilled cobblers are superior to one Zhuge Liang.'

iii. Act One Scene Two

This particular drizzly London evening, we sit in a circle to discuss Phoebe's story. Hers involves three Singaporean Chinese sisters residing in New York, like mine (except mine reside in London). The sisters there have a truculent relationship, like mine. I started my story before she did, and I can't help it. I suspect Phoebe of 'borrowing'. In her story, the sisters had opened a French nouveau restaurant. My sisters battle over a steamboat, droll compared to high-stylin' gourmet cuisine. It's such a cliché too – Malaysians and Singaporeans obsessed with food; it's practically our national culture to polemicise food.

Phoebe says with triumph, if David Henry Hwang's Yellow Face was a white 'Siberian Jew' playing the character of an Asian American, Phoebe's White Face was a 'Frenchman of peasant stock' playing the executive chef of a French restaurant.

Miranda looks lost. But Wei sits up straight, as if someone has zapped him with a divining rod. Kevan does what Kevan does – this particular occasion, he is doodling, drawing spirals and faces with no discernible features but with awesomely-styled hair.

Lookie the smirk on Phoebe's face as she takes in Wei's response. I interrupt her flow of verbiage, 'Can we get to what the problem is, Phoebe?'

'Well, I'm stuck.'

Miranda closes her eyes. She often does that during our discussions – for optimal osmosis.

'A New York food critic comes to dine and insists on going back into the kitchen, to talk to the executive chef. Well, she discovers something fishy.'

'So, what's the problem?'

'I don't know what that something fishy could be.'

Wei stands up suddenly. He brings one hand curled into a fist against the upturned palm of his other hand. The gesture makes a *pock* sound. 'I know!' He paces two three steps around our sitting area, then reverses. 'French cuisine is all about the sauces. You could have your Frenchman fuck that up when being asked about how he made the sauce for the duck l'orange or something. How could a French gourmet chef not know something so fundamental?'

43

'Yes! Yes! Yes!' Phoebe bops up and down on the sofa. 'That's brilliant, Wei.'

Miranda, despite eyes being closed, makes a small grimace.

'Isn't that a little gimmicky? And trite?' I say.

Wei and Phoebe look at me, and carry on brainstorming. I look at Kevan, whose spirals have now transmogrified into matchstick figures tossed orgiastically together. Not too long back, Kevan and I had a tête-à-tête – he says he has trouble making eye contact, he's not sure where this overwhelming diffidence suddenly came from, but ethnic diasporic writers sometimes have this crippling self-doubt about the lack of authenticity in their narrative voice. 'If it's all a lie anyway, you might as well make it a big lie.'

'Frauds should stick together,' I'd said.

Kevan smiled. We understand each other. The kind of 'understand' that ended up resulting in a regrettable one-night-stand. We work hard to maintain a facade of it-never-happened.

At the end of our gathering, Wei and Phoebe have decided to work on Phoebe's story together and turn it into a theatrical farce. Not that they've ever even written a play. Or have any clue how to write one.

iv. Act One Scene Three

It's Wei's turn. Wei says he's thinking of using the Chinese coded references 'portioned peach' or 'cut sleeve' to signal his protagonist being gay. It's kinda neat that these are literary allusions: 'Portioned peach' as a reference to Long Yang, a youth so well-loved by one of the Kings during the Chinese Warring States Period (475 to 221 B.C.) he shared the King's peach. 'Cut sleeve' is a reference to an Emperor of the Han dynasty who would rather scissor off his sleeve than awaken the male concubine sleeping on it.

Phoebe, Miranda and I all look at each other. An unexpected cold front and it's drizzling outside. Miranda is snuggled up in a cape shaped like an enormous sherpa blanket while Phoebe looks chic in her Burberry trench. Kevan's sweater probably has years of breadcrumbs embedded within, a veritable garden patch.

'I think it's a problem writing about a gay protagonist if you're not gay; isn't that appropriation?' Phoebe asks.

'More to the point: can short stories have footnotes?' Wei asks.

None of us answers. We blink.

'Well, there's this dictum that anything that takes a reader out of the story is non-kosher,' Kevan weighs in.

'Just put all the footnotes in a meta-story,' Miranda says, chomping on an apple. We are at Le Pain Quotidien and she brings her own fruit but Miranda is not one to care about restaurant decorum.

Wei is scratching his head. 'What about slang? I'd rather not have a Singlish thesaurus along with the story.'

'Don't use Singlish,' Phoebe says. 'It's pidgin, it makes Western readers laugh at us.'

Miranda nods. 'Wikipedia says it's considered low class. A creole language. It disrespects the Speak Good English campaign the Singaporean government has promulgated.'

'Write what you want, Wei. Don't sweat it. Somewhere I read once, some writer said that existential creative anxiety is a sure route to paralysis.'

Wei looks at me gratefully. During our break, Wei joins me outside. It's still raining and the awning of the restaurant is dripping, so we huddle and our shoulders nudge each other. 'I didn't know you smoke,' I say. He pushes his hands into the front pockets of his jeans, scrunching up his shoulders. 'I don't. I just wanted to say thank you.'

'You're welcome.'

'You know, I can't make you out.' His look is contemplative.

I flick off the ash into a potted shrub. 'I'm alluring, issit?'

He laughs. 'You wanna grab a drink sometime? Not with the group, I mean...,' he breaks off, suddenly embarrassed. How cute. Those innocent eyes of his, those shapely lips. Ooof. I hear a tap on glass behind me. It's Miranda and Phoebe. Miranda is scowling, and Phoebe is gesturing for us to come back inside. So *kiasu*, afraid I will pull in front of them in this subconscious race for Wei. It's not sexual, per se, because Phoebe is married and Miranda has a bloke. We just can't help ourselves. It's *liddat lor*.

v. Act Two Scene One

Kevan has suggested we camp out on the grass in Hyde Park – enjoy the trill of birds, the gleam of sunshine, the kerfuffle of toddlers and dogs with wagging tails –and see if our muses will favour us today. Miranda has brought a large thermos of hot chocolate to share. She's done it before, and none of us thinks her hot chocolate is any good – it's thick and sludgy but we don't have the heart to tell her. Phoebe brought a pandan cake. 'You made this?' Miranda is all ready to turn on the fake-surprise.

'No*lah*, I got it from Wardour Street.'

'No wonder, stale,' which got a moue from Phoebe and a 'Priscilla likes it.'

Wei is late. Yesterday evening, he and I had actually made good on our drinking date and I'd met him at a bar in Ealing, where he lives. It was easy to talk to Wei; we started with our personal history but it wasn't long before we got into what it feels like to be Malaysian or Singaporean in the UK – you're a subset (Malaysian/Singaporean) of a subset (Chinese) of a subset (Asian) – and on a fair weather day, the English assume you're a tourist. 'I've been passing through for five years,' Wei laughed, 'In some ways it's fair – I still don't know where Virginia Waters is and I don't like British desserts.'

I agreed. 'Everyday there are social interactions, minute as each individual episode goes, but cumulatively they begin to absorb into your tissue. Little razors handed to you every day.'

'Yeah, when they joke about the size of the Asian male penis as if you weren't there.'

'Accuse you of plagiarism for writing too well.'

'Accuse you of stealing a writing class contact sheet because the famous teacher's contact information was on it.'

'Invisible ethnic person (e.p.).'

'Dating a girl, and her mother keeps confusing your name with the other Asian guy she once dated, even though that other guy was Caribbean Chinese!'

'Cross the street because they'd rather not say hello.'

'The hidden transcript. We act and masquerade, and then we tell the hidden stories amongst ourselves backstage. We laugh aggressively, maniacally. Humour to fend off hurt.'

'We're the heartsick diaspora.'

Wei and I started laughing. For a moment, there was a rhythm, a beat, and that's our hidden transcript. That moment changed into something else when we were paying the bill; the bartender had drawn a little guy with a moustache on the bottom of the bill (representing himself?). I said we should go halfsie; Wei said, the bill or the bartender; I cackled, but then noticed Wei had a little bit of beer foam at the corner of his mouth; he caught the look; the look was exchanged; he leaned over and planted a small kiss on my lips; I said, Miranda and Phoebe thought you were gay, to which he said, that's funny, I thought you were gay, and I said, nope, and he said, me neither and that was when I reached for him, one hand behind his neck, pulling. We went back to his apartment and it became hot and heavy very fast.

'Right,' Kevan's spiky lashes half-veiled his steady gaze on me, 'shall we begin? I think it's Chandra's turn this week.'

'Skip. I haven't progressed at all with my story.'

Kevan: Why's that?

Miranda: Bit distracted *lor*.

Phoebe: Is this an inside joke I'm not getting?

Me: I'm not distracted. I've been busy.

Miranda: Uh-huh.

Kevan, still with the veiled assessing eye. 'Ok fine, I can go first.' His story, he begins haltingly, is about an ethnic writer in Birmingham who encounters Garuda, the mythical half-eagle half-human creature from Buddhist-Hindu mythology. Garuda represents birth or heaven, and is the enemy of snakes which represents the underworld. 'There are lots of stories that reimagine Greek or Western mythology, but not so much Eastern mythology.'

'How's it going?' Miranda asks.

'Well, I think. He's just swallowed a farmer and his tractor, and I'm trying to figure out what he should eat next.'

'Appetites are good,' Phoebe says, 'appetites are page-turners.'

I'm looking at my watch, wondering whether I should give Wei a call. I'm wondering if he hasn't turned up because it might get socially awkward. He'd stopped me last night from going whole-hog, saying he wasn't ready yet. A tent had set up between our bodies, and he said he wasn't ready. 'Okay,' I'd said, 'let's go slow.'

Miranda snaps her fingers in my face. 'Kevan has been saying something to you for the past minute.'

'Did something good happen?' Kevan says. 'You're smiling like a silly goose.'

His smile though is neither silly nor goosey, it's ambiguous and troubling, so I push it away. 'As you all know, I've been writing this story about three Singaporean sisters whose mother visits them in London for the first time. They witness an accident. The story pivots on this, except I'm having the darnedest time trying to figure out what the connection is between the accident and the mother's visit.'

'You want to read a section of it out? Maybe we can help?' Kevan says.

I give him a piercing look. This is against his usual policy. Kevan believes that stories in the process of creation need to maintain pressure – like in a pressure cooker – if you broadcast it too soon, steam escapes, so does momentum and mystery.

'Not really,' I say, 'I think I should let it steep. Oolong makes an appearance in my story.'

Miranda takes up the baton. 'I've progressed from Ben-wa balls to a phone call from the nursery, all good here.'

Phoebe dusts her hands together. 'No oriental objects in mine, thank you very much. I don't care to exoticise my story. It's great – I listen to Nas and Mos Def and Tupac as I iron – old skool rap is *sick*.'

Personally, I thought she sounded stoopid.

'Why rap?' Miranda says.

'Why not rap, you think Asian chickas can't rap?'

'What's wrong with you today? Not everything is a hidden judgment of you.'

'Ladies...' Kevan adds a cautioning tone. And then, Wei is here, arriving with panted breath, in hot leather jacket with a whole lot of suave movement. He drops down onto the picnic rug. Miranda and Phoebe begin to fuss. Hot chocolate? Pandan slice? Free foot tickle? Phoebe jokes. What a tart. I can't take my eyes off him. When he finally meets my gaze, a shiver of feeling passes between us, and I have to look away, and that's when I see Kevan catching it all.

At the end of the session, Kevan asks for a word.

We stand away from the group, underneath a tree shedding blossoms. Some land in Kevan's hair. 'S'up, Kevan?' I watch the others pack up the picnic, horsing around with Wei.

'Is something going on between you and Wei?' Kevan seems careful not to betray any expression, but his shoulders look tense, and the question is loaded with the bilge of incipient animus.

'Nothing is going on,' I say, my face turning hot. 'Why do you ask?'

He paws the ground with the tip of his shoe. He shows me the angle of his chin, the characteristic hooded eyes.

'Kevan, what's this about?'

'It's nothing,' he says, 'not important.'

'Well, I don't think it's any of your business even if there is something between me and Wei.'

A flume of heat rises in Kevan's eyes. 'How can you say that? How can you say that to me?'

Shit. Fuck. It's exactly what I don't want. This excess of feeling. We slept together months ago, once. I thought we had worked it out, clarified like oil and vinegar.

'Ugh..Kevan. No.' Stuffing my hands into my jacket, I see Wei glancing over at us. He waves, like waving a flag. Kevan's eyes hardening, 'See? I knew it.'

'Kevan, really? Don't do this.'

'Don't do what? What did I do?'

I walk away. But there's a boiling, a churning, inside my gut.

vi. Act Two Scene Two

It's a week where I don't hear from Wei at all. I finally send him a text or actually, not a text, just a photo of a poster ad for a rescreening of a movie

I'd heard was wonderful – *Eat Drink Man Woman*. Emphatically no text. A text would feel like begging. He doesn't reply, and he's turned off his notification so the two little WhatsApp tickmarks don't turn green.

This week, we are meeting at a borrowed theatre stage in Chiswick. It's dark and echoey and smells like cardboard or paper products stored for a long time. Kevan hasn't shown up yet, but he and I haven't spoken since our conversation under the shedding blossoms.

Wei and Miranda and Phoebe saunter in together. There's a familiarity in their body dynamics – the laughter, Miranda holding the door open for everyone, the easy slide in through the entrance one after the other, Phoebe giving Wei her friendly elbow-dig, their trooping down the aisle of seats, commenting on the architectural features and how strange it is to be taking over a theatre. An uncomfortable feeling roosts in my sternum.

Me (while looking at Wei): Did you guys come together?

Phoebe: Yeah, there was a Spanish food festival in Pimlico, so we went. Wei and I were trying to come up with some food inspiration for our play. The last week, he's been over to my house every evening, but I have to stop serving him fried rice and teriyaki chicken.

Me: I would've liked to come but no one thought to invite me.

Miranda: Don't look at me, I wasn't invited either. I ran into them at the entrance.

Me: You guys spending so much time together, *doesn't* your husband mind?

Phoebe: I thought I mentioned, we're getting a divorce.

Miranda: Where's Kevan?

Me: A divorce? Miranda, did you know about this?

Miranda: Maybe we should start without Kevan. I have to leave promptly today.

Me: Wei, did you get the text I sent you?

Wei (speaking quickly): Uhm..Phoebe and I have been working on our play. Phoebe and I concocted this entire menu centered around salt – okay, not very French – French nouveau. The point is...

Kevan has come into the theatre silently.

Me: Miranda, how's your story going?

Wei: Did you just cut me off, Chandra?

Kevan: Let's get in a circle on the stage.

(awkward silence descends) We all take a seat in a circle, Wei to my right, Miranda to my left, Phoebe to her left.

Me: You know what, I'm just going to come out with it. Phoebe, I feel hijacked by this divorce news of yours. How could you not tell us?

Phoebe: I don't see that I need to tell the group everything in my personal life.

Miranda: I bought peaches from the farmer's market for us to share. Have a look at these awesome peaches. Perfectly rounded and luscious.

Phoebe (under her breath): Not peaches, again!

Me: What I want to know is, Wei, what the story is with you.

Wei: My story? The teenage boy and the ghost are friends. The story is about friendship. I'm really tired of the love story, aren't you?

Me: Don't you know the Alice Munro philosophy for a good story? The erotic moment as narrative pivot! That's what makes a good story! (far off, the sounds of Chinese cymbals – a dong dong chiang! becoming louder)

Kevan: Miranda, yes, I would like a peach.

Phoebe: She just wants all the spotlight on her. As usual.

Me: You *siow cha bor* you, you're a little backstabber, you know...(a dong dong chiang, dong dong chiang, dong dong chiang dong chiang dong chiang)

Phoebe: Name-calling, slut-shaming, people-blaming/All these games we BAMEs playin'/

Miranda: Why don't we all partake of peach? Or a muffin. Would you like a chocolate chip muffin?

Kevan: The ethnic writer crumbles under the anxiety of influence. He has no one to emulate, so he emulates his father.

Miranda: MARLIN! Let's call a Marlin.

Wei is not looking at me. Kevan is. Phoebe is looking at Wei. Miranda is looking at Kevan. We're all not allowed to look at the person to our right. It's a bloomin' Law School Admission Test (LSAT) question, which I once took.

So who is Wei looking at?

vii. Act Three

Today, we are meeting at Camden Lock. Three weeks since the theatre fiasco, which we don't talk about, like the passive-aggressive e.ps we are. Wei has been MIA, even though Kevan keeps calling him.

Kevan makes us traipse down to view the Robbo wall (we obligingly gawk like crows with open beaks) as he waxes knowingly about the famous graffiti war between King Robbo and Banksy. Then we walk a short distance and rock up at a rather posh eatery, where you can order hummus and falafel at a tenner a pop. Miranda brings out a tupperware of Chinese sesame balls filled with red bean paste. 'Put that thing away!' Kevan hisses. Miranda refuses. We all sheepishly troop out again, with Phoebe mock-bowing to the contemptuous staff.

We end up settling on a small patch of grass overlooking the grim sludge of the canal, just so we can eat the sesame balls. Visitors and tourists are few at this time of the morning, although the day promises to be all lovely sunshine and crisp spring weather. Some mutual eyeballing with a couple of elderly residents out for a walk. Some shooing of pigeons attracted to our food supply.

The sesame balls are heaven! As I bite into one, the rich bean paste has a clayey sweetness that fills my mouth. Suddenly, a memory of home – sitting at a hawker's centre early in the morning with my grandmother, the ceiling fan above whirring and creating a ripple across the scrim of *kopi kosong* in my coffee cup, my grandmother who is racist to my face and calls me a mongrel, but who loves me so unconditionally she once threw herself in front of a moving trolley full of mandarin oranges when I was six, and then joked, despite her bruises, that it was raining gold.

Maybe it's the sesame balls. Maybe it's the resident on an anchored houseboat out watering her plants who sees us and waves with her watering can. Maybe it's the incongruity of the couple walking past – man in colourful Caribbean clothing with dreadlocks, woman in a generic parka dragging a little girl along walking a toy dog as if it's a real one. The hodge-podge feels natural and right, as does my cheesy Chineseness.

This would have been an epiphany of sorts if Kevan hadn't opened his mouth. 'We need to take a decision,' he says, 'no more hanky-panky within our group.'

'What do you mean – hanky-panky?' Phoebe says.

'Or sexual intrigue.' Kevan eyes me accusingly.

'Is that why Wei says he left?'

Kevan sighs. 'He hasn't left. I'm just saying that it kinda ruins the camaraderie. Besides, it's incestuous. We're too small a group, too intimate.'

'How incestuous? We are not siblings, just minorities from the same continent.' Miranda says.

'Regardless, we take a decision today. Either we swear off sex with each other (previous acts are grandfathered) or we join the bigger meet-up group – the British Asian writers.'

That takes the cake – the sub-subset swallowed up by the subset.

Kevan calls a vote, and I voted for sex.

I'm the odd one out.

GERRY McKEAGUE

Wet Bloody Country

'Are you sure you want to let the boy go with Jackson? I'd not let him take the boy to the shop, never mind Donegal.'

Aunt Eileen spoke through a mouthful of toast, adjusted the headscarf on her forehead. She was like an older version of my mother, only one more likely to raise her voice, who didn't care how roughly her words landed.

'And hasn't he probably stolen the keys off some poor bastard,' she went on, 'or won the fuckin' thing in a game of cards?'

My mother's hands reached for the unused cutlery on the table; they straightened the knife and fork in front of her, shifted the spoon a notch so it squared everything off at the top.

'Go up and pack your bag, Colm,' she said.

My washed clothes lay on my bed, ready for the journey. I sniffed my t-shirt and shorts before I pushed them into the corner of the small red case. From the back of my wardrobe I took my swimming togs and on top of the pyjamas threw a tennis ball, three conkers, a 'Dublin Zoo' cap and a handful of cowboys my father had given me; he'd owned them since he was a boy. One face looked like it had been chewed away.

My mother's voice reached me.

'I've made my decision,' she said. 'Jackson's trying hard. And where's the harm? It's only for the weekend.'

This place we were going to would be different from Belfast. I imagined us walking, my father and I, alongside a stone wall before he bent down and joined his fingers so I could throw my leg over a pony. I thought then maybe not a pony, but a ride on a funfair, the pair of us laughing as we smashed into other boys with their own daddies, reflected lights shimmering across the dodgem car. Afterwards, it would be so hot our shoes would stick to the tarmac and we'd have to take them off and run down a sandy path until we'd come to blue water. We'd go in for a swim, feel the sun on our faces. Maybe he'd buy us ice cream from an old fashioned seller, a big man with a moustache that curled at the corners, pushing a barrow along the sand.

I stared at the suitcase until a car's horn sounded in the street. The shout came up the stairs:

'That's you now, Colm!'

Outside, my father had opened the boot, was pushing bags aside to make space for mine. He took his sunglasses from his pocket and put them on. He was wearing shorts and a red T-shirt with a palm tree on it. The car's blue paintwork dulled as two clouds shifted quickly above us.

'I hope you get the weather you're expecting,' my aunt said, coming out onto the front step.

'How's Eileen?' my father said, like he didn't really want to know the answer.

'Surviving.' She folded her arms in front of her chest. 'I'd love to be gallivanting off on holidays, but some of us have to work. Do you know where yez are going?'

'A caravan this side of Buncrana,' he said. 'A lovely spot.'

My mother stepped onto the street with us, put an apple in my case and zipped it closed. As she offered it to him she held onto it for a moment, wouldn't let it go.

'It'll be grand, Mary,' he said as he took it from her. 'He's going to have a ball.'

'It's his first time on his own.'

'He's not on his own.'

Aunt Eileen sighed behind us.

'Look after him, will you, Jackson?' my mother said.

'Of course.'

'Can you get him home by dinner on Sunday?'

'I'll get him back,' he said, 'good as new.'

He leaned back against the car and smiled at her.

'You know we've space for one more. We could all make a holiday out of it.'

'You tell your daddy,' she said to me, 'you want to talk to me any time and he'll get me on the phone, alright pet?'

The car smelt of cigarettes. A 'Racing Post' had curled on the floor. I wanted to be in the front with him, but my mother made me sit in the back where the leather cooled my thighs. The two women waved from the doorstep until we turned out of the estate.

'Are you all set, pardner?' asked my father, glancing in the mirror. He slapped the steering wheel, like we were going on the road for a long time.

'Sure am,' I tried in an American accent, but it came out wrong.

Before we joined the motorway he pulled in.

'Right you be,' he said, patting the empty seat next to him. 'Come in here.'

'I have to be in the back seat,' I said. 'Mummy told me.'

He pretended to look under his seat.

'Is she here now? Do you not want to see what's going on?'

I climbed over his bag and he pulled the seat belt around me. I could see much more in here; I could look out the front and watch the road coming towards us.

We drove down the slip road onto the motorway where I began to count the blue telephones at the side of the road.

'There's a mile between each of them,' he said.

I asked him how many phones until Donegal.

'About a hundred,' he said.

He turned the radio on and we listened to two men shout about how good a football match was; in the background the crowd made a noise like a huge wave going up and down until we reached another town and crossed a bridge with two layers on it. We took the lower one where it was darker and noisier; the metal slats all blurred together.

On the other side, when the houses disappeared, we queued on a narrow road until a soldier put his hand up and we stopped.

'Off somewhere nice?' he asked and leaned backwards, like he might treat us to a limbo dance. His eyes shifted around our car, from the bag of food, the rolled towels, my father's Spurs football bag in the back seat, into where I sat; he winked at me.

'Taking the wee lad on his holidays,' my father said, handing over a thin blue book for the soldier to read.

'Where to?' the soldier's gloved fingers turned the pages quickly.

'Buncrana,' my father said.

The soldier walked to the front of the car and read our number plate. He talked into the radio on his chest, like he was speaking to his own armpit.

'Have a pleasant holiday Mr O'Callaghan,' said the soldier, like he knew who we were.

'*Slan abhaile, you bollox*,' my father said, after we'd left the soldier behind.

Now we were in the 'Free State,' the road felt different; it was narrower, the surface made the car shake and yellow lines marked the centre. White and blue bags dotted the fields on top of a mountain.

'That's to hold the cut turf,' my father said.

He pulled out to overtake a tractor which a boy, not much older than me, was driving. The boy waved at us. My father's hand reached for a lever and my seat went back so I could look at the ceiling. It was stained dark yellow in parts and the plastic light was cracked in half. I must have fallen asleep then because when I woke up we were coming into someone's driveway.

'Wait here,' he said and disappeared into a bungalow. My eyes searched the hedges and low grey walls for our caravan. All I saw was this garden with its windmill and fountain. He came outside, waving a key in the air like it was treasure he'd found under one of the gnomes.

Up the road, he got out to open a gate into a field. We rumbled over rough ground towards two caravans which faced each other like a caravan shootout at a Donegal corral. We slowed at the shiny red van with its clean windows and fancy decking, but didn't stop, kept driving towards its dirtier reflection with faded blue paint, propped on bricks and guarding a small wood. My father's boots came off at the doorway and his toes wriggled through matching holes in his socks.

'Get your shoes off, wee man.'

I squinted and a sofa appeared from the gloom; a spring had poked through a cushion and hung loose, almost reaching the thin yellow carpet.

He found two mugs in the cupboard and pumped his foot into the floor, made water pulse from the tap.

'When are we going to the beach?' I asked.

He took a swig of water and picked at his chipped mug.

'Tomorrow,' he said.

'Can we get ice cream?'

'As much ice cream as you like, pardner,' he said.

The bedroom smelt of old people's clothes. I unrolled my sleeping bag next to his on the double bed. He whacked pillows and made tiny dust clouds appear. His fingers undid the window latch and forced it open.

'It'll be grand,' he said, 'with some air around the place.'

While he made tea, I explored the field. Behind our caravan, leaves dripped loudly. A warm wind blew off the road and bent the tops of the trees. I went across to our neighbouring van, which I'd decided to call 'Big Red.' A small bicycle, its handlebars gleaming, leant against the side. Almost before I realised, my hands reached for the grips and I swung a leg over the frame. What would it be like to ride down the hill towards the beach? I pushed the bike away from the van with my foot and freewheeled to the gate. A car passed and I saw a white finger lift off the steering wheel. Its engine softened as it turned the corner. I'd never ridden on the road before. I turned the front wheel around and pointed it back towards our caravan. My belly ached as I pedalled up the hill.

He let me drink lemonade with supper. He pulled the ring on my can, scraped corned beef from a tin onto our plates. This wasn't like any supper

I'd had before. The more I ate, the thirstier I got. After my last mouthful, I got up to take my plate to the sink.

'No rush,' he said. 'They'll do later on. Come out with me till I've a smoke.'

He jabbed his cigarette upwards at stars as they appeared in the sky.

'That's the Plough. And d'ya see the Great Bear?'

Our caravan's light had fanned across the field towards our neighbour. Could the owners be in town tonight? Maybe they were eating ice cream on the Prom, a mummy and a daddy and another wee lad.

My father rubbed the grey hairs on his cheek.

'How's your Ma doing?'

'Hunky-dory,' I said.

With his thumb he flicked ash on the grass; a crackling laugh came out of his chest.

'She's told you to say that. She's some woman. Anyone calling to see her these days?'

I stared at where the ash had landed. This was only our first night. What other questions might there be?

'I'm sorry, wee man,' he said. 'I shouldn't be asking you.' He flicked his cigarette away. 'Time to hit the hay.'

I'd seen him only a handful of times since he'd walked out on us one rainy Wednesday afternoon, two years earlier. Sometimes he'd call for an hour or two on his way to another place. On my birthday there was a phone call from Manchester.

'I'm helping them rebuild a football stadium,' he'd said, like the job depended on him alone. 'I'll take you on a wee holiday when I get back.'

The next morning, as much I wanted to stay in my sleeping bag, my hands unzipped it and my feet swung onto the carpet. The bigger sleeping bag was empty but I heard him whistling. I pulled back the curtains and looked across the field towards Big Red which still had its curtains closed, no car parked outside, the bike where I'd left it. Branches scraped our roof; a gust of wind made the caravan shudder.

My father's grey hair was standing almost straight up on his head. Spittles of rain blew across the open doorway. He pulled on an old army type jumper and opened silver paper, snapped a chocolate bar in two. A bag of crisps emptied onto our plates. He lifted a steaming pot from the hob and poured hot water into cups, spooned two sugars into each.

'Are we still going to the beach, Da?'

'Bet your life, wee man. Sure haven't we ice creams to get?'

We brought towels, a fishing net, a blanket and a packet of custard creams. We were halfway to the sea when he pulled off the road. In front of an old church, a car had broken down.

'Need a hand?' my father asked.

A man was rubbing a spanner with a cloth.

'Aye, we're a bit stuck.' The man nodded towards his car. 'Do you know anything about engines?'

'I hope so,' my father said. 'I'm a mechanic.'

'Do you hear that, Rose?'

A woman stepped out of the car and sat on the stone wall. The two men discussed the engine. The woman lit a cigarette.

'Isn't it great,' she said, 'that you've a daddy who can fix things? He must be a handy man to have at home. Your mammy's very lucky.'

She was dressed like she was on her way to a night out, a dance. She wore bright red lipstick and her nails were painted a dark colour which might have been black. While my father and the man tried to fix the car, she scolded:

'Didn't I tell you to get that rattling seen to, Sean?'

'Give my head peace,' the man said.

'You leave everything to the last minute,' she said. 'We should have come by bus!'

She winked at me.

My father asked if they'd anything he could use for a tie.

'I've no rope or string, nothin',' the man said.

'Have you tights on, missus?' My father asked.

The woman stepped out of her shoes and began to unroll her tights, laughing when she almost fell over.

'Jesus wept,' she said.

'Start her up, there,' said my father, once he had fastened the tights around something. The engine chugged a few times like it wasn't going to start, but it came to life.

'Just in time,' said the woman as the sun disappeared.

A plastic bag of cut cables and tools began to rustle and I realised it had started to rain. We'd not make the beach now, I thought. Maybe we'd have the ice cream indoors.

'Get in you fellas out of that day,' the woman said.

My father's hand slapped their car roof as they drove off.

'That'll do yez till Ballybofey, anyway,' he said.

Out the window, the woman's fingers made a fluttering wave.

'Take her easy!' I shouted, which made my father laugh.

Rain hit the windscreen in thick gusts as we drove towards the Prom. Grey clouds hung low over the dark sea. In the wind, tall grass bent one way and another. We parked by the steps. Rain came sideways past the window and needled a pool where stone pelicans stood, getting battered by the weather. In a box, an orange life-ring with a piece missing clattered as it lifted in the wind. Maybe a shark had bitten into it, I thought and imagined a dark shape swimming beneath the water until my father said:

'Such a wet bloody country,' and started the car.

On the street, our car drove slowly against the rain, past some people who'd taken shelter in doorways, or come out to open umbrellas on the street and huddle together to stay dry. The car in front drove on, made a space open up. We didn't move. From behind, a horn blew. I followed my father's eyes towards the men smoking outside the doorway, into the shop with its flickering TV on the wall, the horses running. The other horn blasted again, we began to move and drove until we reached our field.

Though we'd walked through the mud, this time he didn't take off his boots. Back and forth he walked the carpet, his fingers clicking together like there was music playing in his head.

'Will we do something?' He said suddenly and opened drawers until he found a box of draughts. 'Here we go!'

We were two pieces short so he used a match and a coin. I think he let me win the first two games, before beating me in the third. I went to the window, then, because the water was coming against it in such waves I thought there must be someone out there, a hose turned on and pointed at us. I rubbed the condensation away but there was no one, just the rain falling on us all. Over at Big Red, the bike's wheels were slowly disappearing in a growing puddle. As I turned, my eyes fell on a deck of cards on the shelf.

'Can we play with these, Da?'

He had set up draught pieces for a new game.

'You could teach me,' I kept at him.

He stretched his fingers in front of him, like it was the first time he'd seen his own hands.

'Give them here,' he said, finally and began to shuffle them. The cards moved from one hand to another like a fan. When he split the deck in two, he flicked his thumbs back so the cards magically mixed together, and then we played. A king came down on a king.

'Snap!' I shouted.

We played until it became difficult to make out our cards. When he noticed me staring at the fridge, he stood up.

'Alright, wee man. Tea time.'

From the fridge came last night's leftovers; he pumped the floor to wash two plates. He spooned out the rest of the corned beef.

I took only one mouthful before I pushed my plate away.

'I'm not hungry.'

His eyes moved from my plate to his, to the tin of corned beef, to his own hand holding the spoon.

'Let's go for a run into town,' he said.

We parked above the beach, sidestepped puddles as we walked the footpath until we reached the pub. There was a rack of antlers for our coats, pictures of hurling teams on the walls, green leather seats surrounding clean polished tables, and a fire burning.

'A wild evening,' said the barmaid. 'Will yez be eating?'

'Indeed we will,' my father said and took the menu. He pulled out a stool for me which was so high I thought he'd lift me up.

'A big boy like you can climb up, rightly,' he said.

The barmaid brought me a lemonade and a pint of Guinness for my father. I watched the white head grow slowly in his glass and the idea came to me that I could easily lick it off.

'Chowder for me and your finest ham and cheese toastie for His Nibs, please,' he said.

'Grand,' said the barmaid. 'How long are ye staying?'

'The weekend, just.'

'Shame you weren't here for the bank holiday,' she said. 'We'd lovely weather.'

'Ah sure,' my father sipped his pint so the stubble above his lip turned creamy white. 'Only a fool would rely on the weather. You take the rough with the smooth.'

The toasted sandwich came with big crinkled crisps. The chowder was steaming.

'Just the ticket,' my father said, cheerfully.

'Has the wee boy been down to the beach?'

'We drove there but couldn't get out,' he said and paid for our meals. 'We'd have been blown back to Andytown.'

'It gives showers for tomorrow, too,' she said and took a newspaper from under the counter, pushed it towards him.

'There's a fine cinema in the town,' she said. 'There might be something the wee boy'd like to see.'

'*Go raibh maith agat*,' he said, but when she left to serve another customer, he didn't open the cinema times. Instead, he found the back pages where the writing was small. His brown stained fingers moved along the lines.

'Have you found anything?' she asked.

'I've forgotten,' my father said, 'something in the car. Can I leave him here for five minutes?'

'I don't know,' she said.

'He's still eating his sandwich. I don't want to rush him.'

He slapped the bar as he stepped from his stool.

'I'll be back in a wee minute,' he said.

'You're welcome,' said the barmaid as he left us to go out to the street.

I slowly picked at my sandwich, pulling the ham out with my fingers. A TV on the wall blared out questions from a quiz show, what was the capital of Denmark?

'Maybe you'd like some cake?' asked the barmaid. 'There was a birthday party and we've leftovers.'

She brought me a slice of girl's cake, pink frilly icing and half a princess's crown on it, with another drink of lemonade. I imagined children at the party running around. While I ate, I read a poster on the wall, some Irish mother writing to her son. It was the stupidest thing I'd ever read. I stared at the wall behind the bar where all sorts of money was pinned up; big green pound notes, and smaller blue and brown bills. I counted thirty four notes until the barmaid asked if my mammy had come on holiday with us.

'She's at home,' I said. 'Daddy's looking after me now.'

'If you feel like anything more,' she said, 'just let me know.'

Two other men came in then, each ordered a pint and a 'wee whiskey chaser.' They drank quickly, said little to each other or the barmaid. One of them winked at me on the way out.

'You're a good fella waiting for your mammy to finish.' he said, nodding his head towards the barmaid, who kept washing the glasses.

After the barmaid had lifted each chair and clattered it on the table, she mopped the floor so it gave off a sweet smell and shone all around me. Once the till rang shut she turned a key in the bottom.

'Would you happen,' she said, 'to know your mammy's telephone number?'

I shook my head.

'My daddy will know,' I said.

The light was bending across the doorway. I waited for the moment when he'd appear and block it with his shoulders.

'Will you have a bun?' she said, hitching her handbag over her shoulder.

'No,' I said.

'You're not hungry now I suppose,' she said and lifted the phone, turned the dial. She talked softly into the receiver.

'Hi May. Can I ask if you've a fella in there with you?' she said, 'Tall fella, grey hair and wearing a green pullover, patches on the elbows like them army ones?'

The floor polish didn't smell so good anymore; it had gathered in the back of my throat and I wanted to cough it out.

'When did he leave? I've the child here and I don't think he's coming back for him,' she said, turning her back to me. 'And I've no one to phone.'

After she'd made another call and told them about me, the doorway did fill then, the light did block out, but it wasn't my father.

'This is one of the Guards, Sergeant Malone. Would you like to go a walk with him?' the barmaid said. 'You can talk to your mammy.'

The Guard took off his cap and asked me if I was enjoying my holiday. I told him my father was just away a message and we were going to have an ice cream later.

'Do you know where your daddy's car's parked?'

I nodded.

'Could you take me there?' he said, pulling my jacket from the antler.

I stayed on my stool. I stared at my empty glass and began to cry.

'Och, pet,' the barmaid said and reached for my hand. 'You'll be alright.'

'Thanks Grainne,' the Guard said, helping me down. 'I'd say we'll be grand.'

I followed him as he weaved between the tables and green chairs towards the door. When we came outside, a sharp smell of drying rain came off the footpath. I wasn't sure whether or not to take the Guard's hand but it felt like it didn't matter. A dog's head poked from the passenger window of a passing car. Tyres shushed along the road. Some people had removed their coats and slung them over their shoulders. I could smell their fish and chips. Down at the beach, a man and woman lifted a child between them, the child's laughter carrying up to us.

'Maybe we've made a mistake,' the Guard said, when we reached the empty parking space. 'It's probably up at the other end.'

But I knew there was no sign of him here, his car or my father. We returned to where the prom ended. A one-legged seagull hopped around us before it flew towards an ice cream van parked by the seawall. A girl reached up for a cone, sauce running down the ice cream.

'Do you think,' the Guard said, 'you could show me where you've been staying?'

I went beside him in the blue car with 'Garda' on the side and brought him to our field; we drove over the bumpy ground. There was no sign of the car here, either. His big hands shook the door handle a few times but it didn't open; I waited for the pulled curtains to twitch, for my father to come out laughing, that it was all a big mix up. The Guard cupped his eyes with his hands and peered inside for a long time. After he came back to the car he buckled me into my seat, whistled out through his lips.

'I know what we'll do. We'll go for a cup of tea at the station and get your mammy on the phone.'

I stared at Big Red and thought that there was no one staying in it this weekend. Under one of its windows I noticed a crack, the paint peeling away from the door so I could nearly go over and pull it off myself. The bicycle looked different too; I saw now the chain was rusted and the tyres no longer looked new, but worn down, almost bare.

KAREN ASHE

Crossing

In the morning, the police came, stepping across the threshold soft as cats. They swept the place with their eyes, not finding so much as a speck of dust, not a knife dripping on the draining board. It wasn't dust or knives their eyes sought, Gloria knew. Their eyes were out for the one-horned goat, the blood-red candles, the black needle cut from a sliver of slave bone. If they were relieved or disappointed, Gloria couldn't say.

You know about the body?

Course.

A raised eyebrow. *Why 'of course'?*

Mamma took a long draw on her cigarillo, eyes on him like hot coals. Tongues of smoke unfurled from her half-open mouth into the space between the two of them. He tugged at his shirt collar, bravado breaking like summer heat. Mamma shifted on the couch, tucked her legs up under her. He licked his lips. The other two stuck their hands in their pockets, scuffed the floor with the points of their shiny shoes. He flicked over to a new page in his notebook, looked quick at Gloria, back at mamma. Mamma flicked ash into her cupped hand. *It's all anybody can talk about.*

And you didn't hear a thing? This close to the tracks, you didn't hear a thing?

Gloria lived with her mamma in a two-room shack at the junction of the road and the railway. There wasn't a true right angle in the whole place, not two planks sitting straight. It shook and rattled as the freight trains flew past, horns blaring, lights pulsing. Everything they had was either tin or plastic; anything else shattered. Gloria had learned to sleep through the noise, and barely noticed it, even in the day.

This was a passing-through place, not a place for getting off. Or on, for that matter. Gloria would sit among the wildflowers that sprouted by the side of the tracks, arms wrapped round her knees, looking at the long stretch of rails sliding towards the horizon till the only sign of them was the glint of sunlight on the metal.

Their toilet was out back. If they needed to go in the dark, they went together, shining a flashlight into the trees. In case nature called in the dead of night, they kept plastic buckets under their beds; mamma didn't want her getting caught in the yellow lights of the trains as they hurtled past.

The pittance her mamma earned from the sewing she took in put food on the table, not much else. But she sent Gloria out to school every day in a clean skirt and blouse. It was a five mile walk, and Gloria walked it every day, twice a day, rain or hail, sunshine or snowfall.

Her seat was at the back, an empty chair her classmate. None of the children wanted to sit with her, and Miss Lamb wouldn't force them. Gloria didn't mind too much. She didn't feel too lonesome if she had a book to read. It was hard to figure, though. Stinky Lucy always had someone to sit next to. Crazy Mary with the glass eye always had someone to eat lunch with. Johnny Smash, who spent most of the day banging his head on the desk, was never short of company on the walk home.

Gloria almost always scored full marks; sometimes she lost a mark if Miss Lamb thought her penmanship a little lacking, or her punctuation not quite up to scratch. Miss Lamb never remembered to give Gloria the gold star for full marks, so it didn't get marked on the chart for the end of year prize handed out by the headmaster.

Gloria liked sitting at the back. None of them could sneak up behind her, press their hands on her hair and ask in their wondrous voices *It's so foamy. Why is it so foamy?* Her mamma rubbed eucalyptus oil into her hair every night, her long fingers stroking her scalp, lamplight falling quiet all around them. Once, she walked all the way home with feathers and glitter in her hair, hadn't even known. Mamma had slapped her upside down when she saw her, for allowing it. But how can you not allow something you don't even know is happening? Mamma gave her extra bread pudding that night, and let her stay up reading an extra half hour.

One time they pinned her against the wall in the yard, and with a sharp-edged stone drew blood from her arm. They wanted to see what colour it was. Geniuses. She wasn't quick enough in hiding the mark when she got home. Mamma held her by the wrist, examined the shallow wound, crusty with dried blood. Gloria flinched, expecting to get slapped up again, but mamma just told her to go dab it with juniper leaves.

Next morning, they were just getting going on the arithmetic, when Gloria was startled by sight of her mother just outside the yard. In a yellow dress printed with sprigs of honeysuckle, her hair smoothed back into a tidy bun, she looked like she was about to take a pie out of the oven in a gleaming white kitchen. Gloria glanced around; nobody else had noticed. When she looked back Mamma was gone, striding up the road with the dust spraying from her heels.

Next morning Gloria found herself at the back of an empty classroom, every one of them laid low by a ferocious vomiting bug. Gloria vowed never to let mamma find out anything that happened to her ever again.

After that, Miss Lamb decided that it would be better for Gloria to stay indoors at lunchtime, eat lunch at her desk, 'to avoid... – she searched for the word – 'contamination.' When they left the window open a crack, she could feel the cool air against her cheek. She could hear the click of the jump rope on the ground, the scud of a ball on good school shoes. Once, a stray dog got in to the yard and she could hear them all screaming and yelling, throwing rocks to get rid of it.

*

About halfway home, she was lost in her own quiet thoughts. The long grass was crackly in the dry heat. The sun was low, bright in her eyes as a searchlight.

A shift in the air behind her stopped her dead. Slow, and with the worst of dread, she turned her head.

Heat shimmering off the wheat spears, off the straight white fence poles strung with wire. The fretful chatter of small birds, clouds creeping across the sky, screech of unseen insects. Sweat bloomed on her skin, sticking her blouse to her back.

She pushed on. Hadn't gone two steps, when an arm swept her feet from under her. She hit the dirt with a thud, a knee in her back kept her there. A sack was pulled over her head. She was flipped onto her back. Hands gripped her wrists, forcing her arms above her head, hands on her thighs shoved her skirt up to her waist.

She'd done everything mamma told her. Never rolled her skirt up above her knees. Never opened a top button. Always stuck to the middle of the road or the open field. But here it was, happening anyway.

She squirmed and twisted, bucked her hips. Her breath sucked the sacking into her mouth. *Hold her tighter, chrissakes! I'll never get em off her if she's movin.* She felt a squeeze on her wrists, then the bones of two soft knees pressing on them. She felt the blood thicken and pool there, the throb of a thwarted pulse. Her fingers went numb. She kicked her legs and twisted but the hands were up at her waist, then there was a tug and her underwear was off. Whole thing didn't take more than two seconds.

Hands grabbed her ankles, pulled them apart. She heard a soft moan, realised it was coming from her. Her attackers were silent, breathing bull-heavy. She could feel the warm air moving over her private parts, and she cried then, thinking about her mamma, and how ashamed she would be to see her lying like that. She hoped no-one could see from the road.

Quit snivellin! It was the one holding her ankles. *Don't make me slap ya...*

Another voice, off to the side, high-pitched and whiny. *See I told ya. Same as white girls...now let's go!*

Then there was a mouth near her ear, a slobbery whisper. *Don't tell nobody about this, half-breed.* He let go her wrists, the other one let go her ankles. *You count to a hundred. Then you can go.* She heard the long grass shift as they moved off, snorting with laughter, in no hurry. With her hands above her head, head in a sack, skirt hoiked up, legs spread, trembling, she counted to a hundred. A hundred sobs. They kept her underwear.

She walked home with her eyes on the ground, sure that anyone who looked at her would know. She told her mamma she felt sick to her stomach and went straight to bed. She stayed in a bed a whole week. Mamma brought chicken broth and mashed potatoes and iced tea with sugar, but she everything tasted like sacking, like dust in the back of her throat. She had an ache in her shoulders from being held down for so long. There was a cuff of bruises on her ankles. Shame rolled over her, crunched her into a ball, as she thought of how she must have looked, lying in that field, exposed. But they hadn't tried to touch her. At school, the kids made exaggerated half-circle swerves to avoid touching her. They must have found her repulsive. She hoped they did. She hoped they weren't coming back to finish the job.

She sat with her mamma, threading the needles, stitching the straight seams, both of them pausing each time a train went past so the jolting wouldn't affect the stitching. Mamma watched her with those violet eyes, but her mouth stayed tight as one of her seams. At night Gloria got on her knees on the bare boards and prayed. She prayed to the Lord to grant her this one thing, if he never granted her any other; that she wouldn't ever have to cross that field again.

Overnight, the schoolhouse burned to the ground. Gloria went with her mamma to look. All that remained was a couple of charred stumps in a hump of black ash, like the last teeth in an old fella's mouth, and the last gasps of smoke. Mamma sniffed. *Well, I guess that's that.* She slapped one hand against the other to seal the deal. Gloria had no desire to anger God with a display of ingratitude, and was careful to give thanks in her prayers, but she might have preferred a miracle that allowed her to continue her education. Still, beggars can't be choosers.

A week later the postman delivered a letter from the Education Authority. In the light of recent events, Gloria Evergood was to attend the school in the next town over, which, in one of those quirks of boundary-setting, was three miles closer, on the other side of the train track.

The teacher was pin-thin, quick as a whip. Gloria's eyes were out to see if she recognised anyone from the old school, but so far, so no-sign. *Ok, take your places everyone!* They all zipped into their seats. Miss Honeywell smiled at Gloria, tapped the only empty desk. *Looks like you'll be sitting here today.* It was right at the front. Gloria dropped into the chair, dizzy from all the newness. She spent the day in an anxious hunch, but in the end there was no glue in her hair, no sign taped to her back.

Next morning, they had to swap places with the person to their left. This happened every morning, so that by the end of the week, there wasn't a kid in the class she hadn't sat beside, and not one of them so much as looked at her sideways. Nobody made stink-face at her lunch. When they played skipping ropes they let her join in, and not just to hold the rope. When she got full marks on her Maths test Miss Honeywell had her stand at the front of the class. She held up the test for everyone to see, pinned a giant gold star to her blouse. Everybody clapped and cheered. Miss Honeywell gave her a sweet out of a jar, a round toffee wrapped in a twist of golden, rustly paper. She slipped it into her pocket for later, spending the whole day in a stew of nerves, squeezing her pocket every two seconds for the reassuring crackle.

She held it in her fist all the way home. *You have it, mamma.*

Mamma gave her a bony hug. *No, Gloria. You earned it.*

Yes I did. So I can do whatever I want with it. Isn't that the rule?

Her mamma smiled at her, shaking her head. *Is there anything I say that you don't remember?*

No, ma'am.

Mamma reached into the drawer, drew out the turnip knife. She paused to let the train pass, then drew the knife through the toffee like it was a block of butter. Gloria took one half, her mamma the other.

She still didn't get invited to anybody's house, or birthday party, or have anyone to walk home with. Everybody was friendly to her, but she had no friends. But she had nobody kicking her lunch into the dirt neither, so she reckoned she had a good enough deal. And no fields to cross.

*

At the crossing she stood waiting for the train to pass. The barrier was down, bells clanging, lights flashing. A small crowd shuffled at her back, impatient to get home. The freight train's whistle scorched the air, and the crowd pushed forward a little, squashing her against the barrier. She felt a thing on her neck, a wasp or a spider, and she went to brush it off. Low and soft she heard; *Remember me?* His lips brushed wet against her ear, and she was flat on her back again, her head in a sack, with the air moving warm and callous across her. His chest pressed against her back, the bones of his hips against her backside. She could smell the rancid stink of him, a dead mouse under the floor. *Been wondrin where you got to.* The bells clanged and the lights flashed. The whistle screamed. At last, she felt the whoosh of air. She counted to twenty, and the train flashed past, a silver blur, and the barrier lifted. And he was gone. The barrier went up and down twice more before she could move.

*

When it got real hot, when breathing felt like drowning, Gloria and her mamma would sit on the scrubby patch in front of the house on two folding chairs, drinking iced water, fanning themselves with two plastic fans. The freight train whistle rode through the twilight. Gloria and her mamma counted to twenty. There was a rush of air that drew their hair back from the roots, then the train, a rattle of metal and noise, tore past.

Nights like that, they slept with the windows open to catch the dawn cool. They slept in their underwear, or nothing at all. Their skin shone with sweat, slippery in the creases at the elbows, the back of the knees. As he crept through the open window, this was what he saw; Gloria, body gleaming in the moonlight, everything all on show. What did she expect, leaving the window open? Sitting out there all night with her skirt hitched up above her knees?

He glanced towards the bedroom door. Open a crack. No matter. If the momma came in, he'd have her too. He moved towards the bed, syrup in his veins, bubbles in his chest. He could really make a night of it here. Maybe he'd go *get* the mamma.

He looked back at Gloria, licked his lips. He'd have had her in the field that day, rest of them hadn't been so chicken. She stirred, rolled over onto her side, showing him her rump, the hollow between ribs and hip. He nodded, smiled to himself. He stuffed the sacking into his pocket. No matter if she woke up. Might be better if she did. If she saw his face. He felt a stirring at that. Imagining her eyes on him. So what if she told. Her word against his. Who's gonna believe a stuck-up half-breed and her white-whore-mamma?

He eased himself onto the bed. Her eyelids fluttered, cute, like a baby dreaming. He reached over and put his hand across her mouth just as her eyes opened. She tried to scream, but his hand sealed her mouth was good and tight. She bucked and thrashed on the bed, jiggling the plump of her thighs and belly at him. He inhaled, blew out through his mouth. No hurry. The bed creaked, loud. With his thumb and forefinger he squeezed her nose shut, just for shits. She stopped fighting pretty quick then.

He stroked her forehead. *Shh. Shh.* She whimpered. Tears rolled out of the side of her eyes. *You need to be quiet now. I'm gonna be here a while.* Her chest shuddered. *Wouldn't wanna wake your mamma would ya?*

He ran his hand down, cupping her cheek, stroking her neck, hand roaming slow, slow, down down, cupping, sliding...

Gloria averted her eyes. She would not look at him, no matter what. Fingers of moonlight painted the ceiling. He shifted his weight, the bed creaked.

A shadow cut across. Mamma. Catching Gloria's eye, she put a finger to her lips. She drew the turnip knife across his throat quick and smooth, like he was the Christmas pig. He never saw it coming.

*

Mamma had him by the ankles, Gloria the wrists. The whistle of the freight train cut through the silent dark. They dropped him onto the tracks, scrambled down the bank. They counted to twenty in whispers, then there was a rush of air that drew their hair back from the roots, and the train, a rattle of metal and noise, tore past. Mamma slapped one palm against the other. *Well. I guess that's that.*

*

Mamma leaned forward. The policeman leaned back an inch. *Son, this close to the train tracks, all you hear is trains.*

AIFRIC CAMPBELL

Karolina

Karolina's dog is gun shy. She says it happened after he snapped his cruciate.

'Out there,' she points at the blackthorn thicket on the far side of the reservoir.

Hanley trembles, pink-rimmed and edgy like Weimaraners do. Like their eyes hurt, like they're allergic to just being themselves. It's hard to look at that and fall in love the way you would with a lab. Like Roxy, for example, who sprawls panting in the wet grass at my feet.

'The vet says it is surgical trauma. Ja, dogs, they can hear things under anesthetic, did you know? Like the saw that cut into Hanley's bone.'

Karolina straightens up, knuckles on hips, her long slender legs straddling my path.

I don't know why she's ambushed my run or why she's even up here on the ridge and not down below with her usual lakeside strollers. I know her set, I've heard her laugh strafe the schoolrun convoy of wellied women who cluster like flamingoes by the open trunks of Discoveries, talking Pilates and exam boards as they shuffle out of their Hunters. I always take the secret deer track from the car park to the solitude of these open fields, through coppiced hazel and bramble, past bluebells and ramsons and yellow archangel. Up here, where the mud is churned into treacherous trenches by caterpillar tread, like the tracks of some giant creature that I imagine roaming the hills in misty dawns.

'But Oliver is not happy with Hanley.'

Karolina smooths a slim-fingered hand over his silver pelt, her wrist manacled with tinkling charms. You can tell a lot about a man's wife from his choice of dog and these two are a perfect match. Ribby and restless, strung tight as garroting wire. Here on the hillside in thigh boots and moleskins with her blue stare and sunshot hair, the lake glittering magnificently behind her. All that's missing is a riding crop. Trophy dog, trophy wife, who'd always be up for a knockabout on the court or a good fuck. Who's seen plenty of fundraisers in little black dresses that should say sexy but instead hang limp on her bony breast. I'm thinking Oliver is a banker/lawyer/surgeon and there was something irresistible about her

Germanness that needed to be taught a lesson. A leather whip, handcuffed to the bed, like that could make up for history.

'Marlene Dietrich,' tumbles from my mouth.

'What?'

'I meant your accent.' Though what I really mean are the plosives that pepper each sentence.

'Hah!' she smirks. 'Veee-aaaaynst-lilleeemaaar–leeeeyn,' and it's a thin uneasy warble. The wind swipes her hair and she yanks it back, stretching her broad pale forehead, pulling the hairline high and tight on the scalp. The effect is a distressing cranial elegance as if her skull might split the skin.

'Tomorrow is Hanley's last chance,' she sighs. 'Oliver has a twenty gun shoot,' she rummages in the pockets of her Barbour and pulls out a gun.

'What the fuck –'

'Starter pistol, silly girl!' She wiggles it, grinning and lets her hand fall to the side. 'We came here to practice. You and me together, Hanley, no?' His bone-shaped dog tag quivers.

'So what happens if – '

Oliver will replace him.'

'Then Hanley can retire and be a pet.'

'No!' she glares down at me like I am some kind of idiot child. 'Oliver only keeps useful things.'

So how long before he trades you in, I want to ask. The crows cackle, bobbing on the overhead wire like they're testing the spring.

'And I have Jett,' she jerks her thumb at the ditch where a spaniel scuttles in the ferns. 'He is eating some new food that makes him hyperactive. Like he's drinking Red Bull, whizzing round the house. Or maybe,' she shrugs, 'he is looking for Maria.'

'Who's Maria?'

'Maria is my cleaner who is drowned.' She tips her head at the reservoir.

'She fell in?'

'She jumped in.'

'How do you know she jumped?'

'Two big stones in her pockets.'

Jett whirls towards us and veers away, snout down towards the hedgerow on the far side. Karolina fondles Hanley's silken ears. 'No one ever thinks about what happens to dogs in a suicide.'

A shout of speckled birds swoops low overhead. The oak bristles behind us and Roxy nudges my shin. A bright blister of light speeds across the lake and I too am keen to go.

'Oliver needs a gun dog.' Karolina dusts her palms briskly. 'He does not need a pet.'

Fuck Oliver, I want to say. 'Tell him it's you or Hanley,' I laugh lightly. But all the same.

'I cannot have any disappointments, because I never expected anything.' She frowns, nodding. 'That is what Marlene had to say in 1959. By then, her accent was melted away. She sounded like a nobody.'

And we share a moment's stillness, Karolina and I, peering into the chasm that separates us. Economic submission. Boredom's silent scream. But that is the life you chose, I'm thinking. Maybe we all just get what we deserve, reap what we sow.

'Will you help?' Karolina turns to face me, flails her arm in a huge gesture. I look down at a lone windsurf, the white and orange sail snuffling out across the water, stippled now by a sudden squall.

'Roxy's not so good with noise.' I offer her a lame smile. 'Like, switch on the Hoover and she's gone.'

Karolina snorts, inflates to full warrior proportions and sweeps me over with arch distaste.

'Sorry,' I mumble, backing away.

'SIT!' she barks. And Hanley does. A tremor ripples through his knotty spine, hair spiked with anticipation. He stares up at Karolina wide-eyed, worshipful and desperate to please, now at the eleventh hour. Then he prostrates himself at her feet with a cringing whine, paws perfectly aligned, head dipped in shame.

'UP!' she roars, belting her thigh and Hanley bolts to shivering attention.

I turn away from this doomed rehearsal and follow Roxy who is already scuttling downhill towards the lake and the possibility of ducks. I jog after, skidding a little as the mud sucks at my boots. Then Roxy stops dead, right in front of me, foreleg raised, ears pricked importantly.

I spin round, right on the shot.

The crows scatter screeching over Karolina's rigid silhouette, her gun still trained on the silver lump at her feet. Jett is an accelerating brown dot speeding towards her and I am running too, mouth gaping, my fingers spread large in front of me, grappling with the air as if I could stop time.

I try to scream at her bending arm, picture myself leaping through the air like a ninja to kick the gun from her hand. But I trip and fall howling, slithering in the mud, just as Karolina tilts her chin skywards and takes her last shot.

CATHERINE CHIDGEY

Black Boys

In 1981, when I was twelve, the Acostas moved in next door. They might have been Spanish, or perhaps Mexican or Italian – nobody was sure. My brother said maybe they came from Chile, where they shot you if you were a Catholic; Sister Benedict had shown us a film about that at assembly. At any rate, they weren't from New Zealand; they weren't from here. My mother baked a batch of her famous melting moments and arranged ten of them on a plate. Ten was a good number, because it left some for us but didn't look mingy. We were going to take them over to the Acostas, except before we could, we saw Mrs Acosta through our net curtains, coming up the driveway. She was wearing a halterneck top and high-heeled red sandals, and over one shoulder, a gold mesh purse on a snaky chain.

My father whistled. 'They don't make them like that any more.'

'Is that an Oroton?' said Mum, and I peered at the drapy purse through the nets. It certainly looked like the pictures in the magazines: women smiling in restaurants, the tables laid with cut crystal and vases of carnations. I went to the door, but Mum hissed at me; we didn't want Mrs Acosta to think we'd been watching her. She counted one one thousand, two one thousand, three one thousand, as if checking the closeness of a storm, then opened the door.

'You have peach tree,' said Mrs Acosta.

'Hello,' said my mother. 'Welcome! I'm Joyce, and this is Melissa –'

'It grows over our fence. Soon it will drop the fruit on our grass. This will rot and attract the flies.'

My mother was still holding the plate of clingfilmed biscuits. 'I'm terribly sorry,' she said. 'Shall my husband cut it back for you?' She was starting to use her telephone voice.

'I have urn,' said Mrs Acosta. 'For preserving of fruit, yes? We make together and keep half each.' She hitched up her gold purse and I saw the mark the chain had left on her shoulder. She smelled of proper perfume, and menthol cigarettes – I recognised the scent from when Tracey Dewar had offered me a puff behind the presbytery. I'd said no thank you, not because I was chicken, but because four other girls' mouths had been on it.

My mother already bottled the peaches; it took her a whole day to sterilise the jars, scrubbing them in the sink, heating them six at a time in the oven. She left them upside down overnight, arranged on boiled tea towels that said *The Welsh Language* and *Canal Boats of the Past*, and we weren't allowed to touch them in case germs from our hands got inside. The next morning she rose early to peel and stone the fruit, then cook it and pack it into the jars. My father looked after tea on preserving day, which meant fish and chips, with peaches and ice cream for pudding, though my mother said she couldn't look at another peach – and besides, she had to watch her figure. 'I'm the same weight I was when I married your father,' she often remarked, running her hands over her hips. She wouldn't let us open more than one jar at a time; they had to see us right through winter.

'Well,' she said now. 'That might be all right.'

'You will pick, yes?' said Mrs Acosta.

'Well,' said Mum. 'Yes, we will pick. Won't we, Barry?'

'Abso*lute*ly,' said Dad.

Mrs Acosta turned to leave.

'Wait – these are for you,' I said. 'Mum's famous melting moments.'

'What are they?' She peered at them. Maybe baking was different where she was from. Julie Azar, who was Lebanese, brought sticky fingers of pastry to school in her lunchbox. She let me try one once, but when she wasn't looking I spat it into my hand.

'Melting moments,' said my mother.

'What does this mean?'

'Ah. How should I explain?'

'A biscuit does not melt. Nor does a moment.'

'She's got you there, Joyce,' said my father.

'It's just a name,' said Mum.

'Except for Dalí,' said Mrs Acosta. 'Dalí makes famous melting moments.'

'I haven't met her,' said Mum, tightening the clingfilm over the biscuits. 'At any rate – for you. No hurry to return the plate.'

*

The peach tree filled the far corner of the garden, its trunk still nailed with steps to a vanished treehouse. It had sprouted from the compost pile before I was born, and when the blossom started falling I used to stand under it and pretend I was a bride. Although Dad never pruned it, never sprayed it, at the end of every summer it grew a vast crop of fruit – black boy peaches, with their startling dark-red flesh. 'Cheaper than Mrs Tenfordollar,' said Mum, which was what we called Mrs Wang the fruiterer. She was always trying to get Mum to buy something extra, but Mum shook her head and said in a loud, slow voice, 'Not on list, Mrs Wang. Don't need.' Then counted her change.

A week after Mrs Acosta's visit, it was time to pick the peaches. The days were still warm but the evening air carried a chill; my brother and I had returned to school, and we knew it was almost autumn. Dad was busy with his Lions project – they were building a viewing platform in the bush so that underprivileged children could look at ferns – and he said he'd pay Anthony and me to do the picking. The feel of the peach skins set my teeth on edge, like chalk on concrete or the word *pantyhose*, so I borrowed my mother's gardening gloves. They were huge on me, and my hands slipped around inside them, but they were stiff, too, and I couldn't bend my fingers properly, couldn't make them do what I wanted.

'You get used to it,' said Mum.

We started on the lower branches, and then we got Dad's ladder. Anthony held it while I climbed to the top rung, even though it had a sticker saying not to.

'I can see up your dress,' my brother called, but I was wearing shorts, and it was just one of those stupid things boys say.

Up among the shifting branches, our house looked different. I saw lichen on the tiles, and scum in the guttering, and a perished tennis ball. Without the light behind them, the butterfly decals that stopped us crashing through the ranchslider seemed dull, cheap. I could see over the fence to where Mr Acosta was digging a big hole. His spade cut and cut at the hard dry dirt, the blade flashing in the sun, sending signals. He wasn't wearing a shirt, and I watched his muscles flickering beneath his skin like fish. I wondered if he and Mrs Acosta would have a baby. I could look after it when they went out to dinner at restaurants, bathing its soft little body, its fuzzy little head, tucking it into its bassinet. I could sing it Spanish songs, my voice high and sad, and it wouldn't notice its mother wasn't there. And then, when it was sound asleep, I could try on Mrs Acosta's clothes.

I stretched to reach the last peaches; it seemed a shame to leave them to split and spoil. Mr Acosta kept digging, and the sound of the spade shuddered through the ground, jolting up the ladder and into my bones. And the sky so bright as I looked for the fruit, and the shove of the spade, and my fingers loose inside my mother's gloves – I felt myself starting to fall, and I grabbed at a branch no thicker than my wrist, and it bowed and bent as I hung there undecided.

'Melissa!' cried my brother, and I knew he was scared, and I called, 'I'm fine I'm fine,' as if he was over-reacting. But I felt a strange churning in the soles of my feet – some old signal, a warning to the body that it's too close to the edge. That was the first time I noticed it, and I still feel it now, in high places – waterfalls, the Sky Tower, the swing bridge we crossed on our honeymoon. 'Mr Acosta,' I called, and he stopped digging and looked around. 'I'm up here.'

'Ah! Yes.'

'Can we come and pick the peaches, please?'

'Of course yes. Come. Come.'

Anthony and I carried the ladder next door and set it up beneath the overhanging branches, and Mr Acosta grabbed it by the legs. 'I hold for you,' he said. A plain gold bracelet shone on his wrist. I'd never seen a man with a bracelet on.

'It's all right, thank you,' I said.

But he insisted, so I ducked under his bare arms and hurried up the rungs, wishing I'd worn something nicer. My hands were hot inside the ugly gloves, and I pulled them off finger by finger, which I'd seen an actress do in a film, and sent them splatting to the ground. They hit Mr Acosta in the face, and I was so embarrassed I pretended I didn't notice. 'How is Mrs Acosta?' I said instead.

'Sadly, my wife is lying down.'

'Oh dear. Is she unwell?' I'd been hoping she would be there; I had some idea we'd be friends.

'Yes. She is unwell.'

There weren't many peaches on their side of the fence – it was the cold side, and the branches seemed stunted; it could have been a different tree. By the Acostas' steps I could see some starlings, their busy shining heads pecking at crumbly chunks of something yellow. As they shattered it into smaller and smaller pieces I realised it was the melting moments.

'Hurry up, Melissa,' said Anthony. 'We'll miss *The Jetsons*.'

It was our favourite programme; we liked to imagine ourselves living in the far future, in circular houses that stood on stalks taller than any tree.

'What is this Jetsons?' said Mr Acosta.

'Just an old cartoon for children,' I said, but Anthony started telling him about the robot maid and the moving walkways.

'It's not real,' I said, climbing back down, trying not to touch Mr Acosta. As I stooped under his arms I willed myself to keep steady, the way I did when we played Operation and I had to tweezer out the wishbone or the heart.

'You don't know the future,' said Anthony.

'Maybe I do.'

'No you don't.'

Just then Mrs Acosta came out with a basket of washing. She was wearing enormous sunglasses like Farrah Fawcett, the lenses purple-black, and when she saw us she stopped and said, 'Oh.'

'Melissa and Anthony are here to pick the peaches,' said Mr Acosta, and she said, 'The peaches,' in a faraway sort of voice, as if she'd just woken up.

She began hanging the washing on the clothesline, taking the pegs from a basket hooked over one of the arms. My mother kept her pegs inside; they got dirty otherwise, and what was the point of washing your clothes if you used grubby pegs? When Mrs Acosta reached up I saw a black bruise on her side, as big as the palm of my hand. She shook out a caramel lace camisole and hung it by its thin straps. How glamorous she was, her hair blue-black in the sun, iridescent as the starlings.

'Mum wants to know if nine o'clock tomorrow's all right,' I said. 'We'll go to Mass tonight, to get it out of the way.'

'What is tomorrow?'

'The peaches. Preserving day. Mum and I are coming over.'

'Preserving. Preserving.'

'In the urn.'

She nodded. 'Nine o'clock, yes.' She turned the clothesline and it let out a long, high cry, and she flinched and said, 'Mateo, can't you fix?'

'Too many things to fix,' Mr Acosta said to us. 'Your father, he has hammer?'

'Yes, he has hammer,' I said. 'He has a hammer.'

'I would like to borrow.'

'It just needs oil,' said Anthony. 'Like a robot.'

'But I have other things, and only two hands.'

'He's out at the moment,' said Anthony. 'Helping the underprivileged children.'

'Who are these children?'

'We don't know them,' I said. 'But Dad's club is building a platform for them, so they can go on healthy walks and enjoy nature.'

'He is good man, your father,' said Mr Acosta, and Anthony and I nodded – yes, yes, a good man, although we'd never really thought about it before.

'I'll ask him about the hammer,' I said. 'I can bring it tomorrow.'

'What's the hole for?' said Anthony.

'The grave of my wife,' said Mr Acosta.

It seemed polite to laugh. Mrs Acosta kept pegging up the washing: a pair of socks, a bathmat.

'No,' said Mr Acosta. 'A goldfish pond. It is ornamental.'

The viewing platform was going to schedule, Dad said, and the opening ceremony was in two weeks. They'd asked someone from the City Council to cut the ribbon; they'd wanted the mayor, but a city councillor was the next best thing.

'What about the deputy mayor?' said Anthony. 'Wouldn't he be the next best thing?'

I told him not to be rude, and he said the deputy mayor *was* the next best thing to the mayor.

'You're such a child,' I said.

'You are. You are,' he said.

'You've done very well, Barry,' said Mum. 'I can't wait to see it.'

'Can Mr Acosta borrow your hammer, Dad?' I said.

'A man like that, without a hammer?'

'They've only just arrived,' said Mum. 'You wouldn't bring a hammer with you.'

'I would,' said Dad. 'First thing in the suitcase.'

He and Mum had friends who'd brought their electric stove with them from England because they didn't think we had them in New Zealand. Dad mentioned it every time we visited. *Lovely scones, Jean. Must be that English stove. Ha ha.*

'Why does he want it?' he said.

'To fix some things for Mrs Acosta.'

'She's not the kind of woman you refuse.'

'She must be homesick, poor love,' said Mum. 'But she hasn't brought the dinner plate back yet. From the melting moments. We're one short.'

'There are only four of us, though,' said Anthony.

'It's a bit rude. She must realise it's part of a dinner set. It was a wedding present.'

'They're just different from us,' said Dad.

'I should have used the Tupperware.'

After tea Dad went to get the hammer. 'One Maori screwdriver coming up,' he said, and I laughed. It was his oldest joke.

The next morning Mum and I packed the peaches in the laundry basket and hauled them over to the Acostas'. I rolled the hammer in a pillowcase so it wouldn't bruise the fruit. We had to make three trips.

'Ah!' said Mr Acosta. 'Why you do not ask for my help?' He was wearing a navy-blue dressing-gown with red piping, like a millionaire.

'You're very kind,' said Mum. Down the hall, stacked along the edge of the carpet, a row of pictures faced the wall, waiting to be hung.

Mrs Acosta was dressed in capri pants and a yellow blouse knotted high on the waist. Her hair was pinned to her head in thick black coils, and plastic bangles slid up and down her wrist. She had a big pot of water boiling on the stove, and it was rattling the lid, *tap-tap*, *tap-tap*.

'I have the hammer, Mr Acosta,' I said. 'One Maori screwdriver coming up.'

'One what?' he asked. 'What did you say?' *Tap-tap.*

'I called the hammer a Maori screwdriver.'

'It is a joke?'

'Yes. Yes, a joke.'

'And how is it funny?'

'Oh.' *Tap-tap. Tap-tap.* 'I'm not sure, actually, but I can ask Dad.'

'Yes. You ask Dad.' He took the hammer, and soon I heard him banging in nails.

'I've brought my own knife,' said Mum, 'for the peeling. You know how we get used to certain things.' She produced the vegetable knife Anthony and I had given her a few Mother's Days ago; Dad had taken us shopping, and we'd all agreed it looked like her. It was serrated on one edge and straight on the other, and the man in the shop said she could use it twice as much.

'No,' said Mrs Acosta. 'I show you.'

She nicked the bottom of a peach, plunged it into the boiling water and scooped it out again a minute later, then pulled the skin away in one piece. Anthony had skinned a mouse like that once, and dried the pelt in the hot-water cupboard, up the top with the Christmas serviettes where Mum wouldn't find it. He said he'd give me twenty cents to kiss it.

'What a good trick!' Mum said now. 'Isn't it, Melissa?'

Mrs Acosta was staring at the skinned peach in her hand. 'What is wrong?' she said.

'Nothing's wrong,' said Mum.

'But it is red. Not yellow.'

'They're black boys. Delicious. Nothing wrong.'

'Another strange name,' said Mrs Acosta. 'Melting moments. Black boys.'

'Maori screwdriver,' called Mr Acosta.

'Is it?' said Mum. 'Well, that's what we call them. That's what they're called in New Zealand.'

She and Mrs Acosta peeled and halved the peaches and I dug out the stones, popping them into my mouth and sucking until they tasted of nothing.

'While I think of it,' said Mum, 'I must get my plate back.'

'It is somewhere,' said Mrs Acosta.

'Just when you can put your hand on it.'

There wasn't much room in the kitchen, and at one point Mum collided with Mrs Acosta, hitting her in the side. Mrs Acosta let out a yelp and her hand flew to where I'd seen the bruise. Mum said, 'Oh my goodness, I'm sorry.' She went to rub it better, but Mrs Acosta leapt away and her blouse rode up and Mum saw it too.

'Are you all right?' she said.

'A little accident,' said Mrs Acosta.

I kept stoning the fruit but the room felt too hot, too small, the sugar syrup boiling on the stove and the urn boiling on the bench. 'Where's your bathroom, please?' I asked.

'Last door on left,' said Mrs Acosta.

Mr Acosta was in the hall, finishing putting up the pictures. As I passed the ones he'd already hung, I saw they were photographs – black-and-white prints of a woman without any clothes on. The way she held her arms and the way the shadows fell, you couldn't really make out her face, and I didn't want to stare.

I hurried past him and shut myself in the bathroom, then dropped some paper into the toilet before I sat down, so he wouldn't hear me going.

When I came out he had disappeared. I stood and listened. Through the door opposite I could see into the master bedroom, and I slipped inside. The bed was unmade, and there were clothes on the carpet, all inside-out and knotted. The gold purse hung on the door, swaying gently, the mesh tiles catching the light like scales. I reached out a finger and touched it, and it was cool and smooth, and when I skimmed my hand underneath I could feel its slinky weight. I listened again: nobody. I unzipped the purse. The pale-pink interior smelled smoky and minty, with a chemical high-note. There was a stub of Lifesavers trailing unravelled foil. Some menthol cigarettes. A gold compact with a dusty mirror, the powder worn down to a ring. A plastic lighter. A pen from a pest-control company. Some bobby pins, one clamped to a long black hair. In a little pocket I found a tube of lipstick, and I wound it all the way up until it pointed to the ceiling like a red finger. I sat on the quilted stool at the dressing-table and dabbed the colour on my mouth, then immediately rubbed it off.

'You want to try?' said a voice, and I jumped. Mrs Acosta was standing in the doorway.

'I'm sorry,' I stammered. 'I was just…I just…'

'Here,' she said. 'Open.' She coloured in my lips, and her fingertips were dark with the juice of the peaches, and I could smell the hot syrup rising from her. 'You see?' she said. 'Beautiful, no?'

I looked at my reflection. I was myself and not myself.

'No?' she said again.

I nodded. 'No. I mean, yes.'

'You keep,' she said, handing me the lipstick.

'I couldn't!' I said, hearing my mother's voice in my own.

'I have many. Is old. You keep.' Then, putting her head on one side, she lifted my hair, twisted it into a rope and fixed it with an ornamental comb like Spanish ladies wear. 'We need more seals, for jars,' she said. 'You go to shop.' And she took some money from the mesh purse.

I wasn't used to wearing my hair up, and the sun felt delicious on my neck. When I was far enough away from the Acostas' I undid the bottom buttons of my blouse, then tied it tight and high on my waist. At the dairy I saw Tracey Dewar, who'd just come from church. 'Wow,' she said, 'you look so old.'

'Thanks,' I said.

'Where were you this morning?'

'I decided not to come.'

'Wow,' she said again, and bought two twenty-cent mixtures of sweets – double her usual, because it was nearly Lent. 'Aren't you getting anything?'

'Probably not.'

'Are you on a diet?'

'I'm thinking about it.'

'I hate my thighs.'

'You're not even fat.'

She bit the head off an Eskimo lolly. 'What are you here for?'

'Jar seals.'

'*Jar* seals?'

'For preserving fruit.'

She gave a hard little laugh. 'I thought you were buying smokes or something.'

On the way back, as I turned into our street, I could see Dad pulling out of our driveway, heading off to work on the viewing platform for the underprivileged children. There was no time to unknot my blouse and tuck it in, so I put my head down and hurried along. I could make out the shape of his car getting closer and closer, and then, when he was a few metres away, he wound down the window and wolf-whistled. He started to yell something, but stopped short when he saw it was me, and his mouth fell open and made a dark hole. Then he was gone.

That night, when Mum and I were doing the dishes, we heard shouting coming from the Acostas'. We couldn't understand what they were saying.

'Did you see the pictures in their hallway?' I asked her.

'No,' she said. 'And neither did you.'

Mrs Acosta brought over our share of the peaches the following afternoon. She was wearing a lot of makeup, but I could see a new bruise jabbed into her cheek.

'Are you all right, love?' said Mum, and Mrs Acosta said yes, of course, though she was sorry to say our dinner plate was broken – a little accident.

'Never mind,' said my mother, too brightly. 'It's forgotten! An accident!'

When she'd gone Mum wiped the jars with a soapy cloth before she put them in the pantry. 'You're not to help yourselves,' she said. 'We need to make them last.'

It was sunny when Dad drove us to the opening ceremony for the viewing platform, but as soon as we started along the bush track we felt the temperature drop, and the ground was slippery with dead leaves. 'Be careful,' Mum kept saying. 'Watch your step.' I was looking down at my feet, trying not to skid, when I heard Dad say, 'Bloody hell.' Just ahead was the platform – but someone had spraypainted rude words and pictures on it, and the other families stood in huddles, shaking their heads.

The ceremony went ahead anyway, the Lions president saying how proud he was of everyone who'd helped, especially when it meant time away from their own children. I looked out over the edge of the platform, into the lush dark gully. I felt that old churning in my feet, and I grabbed my mother's hand. The city councillor made a big show of cutting the ribbon, then said he was pleased to announce that the culprits had already been caught: a pair of Maori boys with nothing better to do – little hoodlums, really – who'd be made to scrub the platform until it was jolly well clean enough to eat off.

For ages, though, you could still make out the shadows of *fuck* and *cock*, until the pine weathered and darkened.

*

I'd started having seconds at dinner, but a couple of hours later I was always hungry again. I took to getting up at night to make myself sandwiches or Weetbix, eating them in front of TV with the sound down low enough that nobody would know. One night, when I'd almost finished a third piece of cheese on toast, I heard a shattering in the kitchen. I couldn't find anything wrong – except when I stepped into the pantry for a piece of banana cake to take to bed, something cut the sole of my foot. One of the jars of peaches had exploded, and the floor was a mess of fruit and syrup and glass. I grabbed a tea towel – *Sights of Aberdeen* – and pressed it to my foot. The house was dead quiet. I didn't make a sound; I wrapped everything in newspaper and hid it at the bottom of the bin. Then I tied the tea towel around the cut and went to bed.

It wasn't better in the morning, and when I uncovered it I saw how deep it was. My father heard me crying, and came into my room. He sat on the bed and said, 'Melly, Melly, what have you done?'

I told him about the exploding jar, and he put his arm around me and said he'd heard that could happen, if something bad got inside, and it was lucky we hadn't eaten them; they could have killed us.

Mum kept me home from school and took me to our GP.

'Now,' said Dr Slate when he'd dressed the wound and told me I was lucky it didn't need stitches, 'shall I see if I have a penny?'

He kept them in his pocket, those huge old coins that were no longer worth anything, and it had been a treat when I was little to feed one to his money-box – a grinning metal figure with a blue bowtie and golliwog hair and the words *Greedy Nigger Boy* pressed into his back. You put the penny on his outstretched hand and pulled the lever and he ate it, his eyes rolling up in his head.

My mother and Dr Slate were waiting for me to reply, so I said, 'All right.'

When I'd done it Dr Slate weighed me. 'At the upper end of normal,' he said. 'Just be a bit careful. Was there anything else?'

Mum hesitated. 'Our neighbours fight a lot. I think –' she glanced at me '– I think he beats her.'

'Mm. How well do you know them?'

'Not well.'

'They're Spanish,' I said. 'Probably.'

'There you are, then,' said Dr Slate.

'I'm worried he'll go too far,' said Mum, and I thought of the hole Mr Acosta had dug in their garden.

'Other people's business is just that,' said Dr Slate.

At home Mum made a pile of cushions for my foot, and that evening Dad brought me a puzzle book and Anthony let me watch *The Brady Bunch* instead of *The Jetsons*. It had just finished when the shouting started up next door. It sounded worse than usual, and then it changed to screaming – a man screaming. Through our net curtains we saw Mr Acosta running up our driveway, the side of his neck pouring with blood. His collar was soaked with it, and all down his shoulder. Mrs Acosta followed, vegetable knife in hand.

'She cuts me,' he yelled when Dad opened the door. 'Whore. Bitch. She fucking cuts me.'

'Now then,' said Dad, 'there are children present.'

Mum spread some newspaper on the floor and then she rang for an ambulance.

Mr Acosta didn't die – the damage was only superficial – and they moved out soon afterwards. I don't know where they went. I used her lipstick for years, until it was so worn down I had to scrape it out with a cotton bud. My first boyfriend said it made me look like Olivia Newton John – at the end of *Grease*, not the start – and I told him it was a present from a murderess.

I remember wondering if Mum would throw out the jars of peaches after what happened. She checked them all, holding them up to the window to see if they'd spoiled, tapping each seal – and then she put them back in the pantry.

One night I must have fallen asleep on the couch; I woke when the Goodnight Kiwi came on TV, climbing into his satellite-dish bed to the tune of a Maori song we'd learned at school. It was a lullaby about a weeping girl, and I was never sure if she stopped crying. I heard someone coming so I stayed there in the dark, and my mother appeared in her wincyette nightie. She went to the kitchen and opened the pantry and reached for a jar of black boys. She unscrewed it and removed the seal – I heard the faint little pop – and then she started to eat the peaches, fishing them out with her fingers, holding her head back and letting the fruit slip into her mouth. I could see her throat ripple and flex, strangely muscular in the pantry's small light. When she'd finished the first jar she opened the next, and the next, and she kept on eating them until the peaches were all gone. Every last one.

PATRICK DODDY

Digging

When the spade is pulled up through the stone-filled clay, it makes a
sharp sound. My hand stays buried until I lift it out: cold and stiff,
tiny streaks of blood across my knuckles, dirt wedged in tracks under
fingernails. My father's fucking hand.

They are coming up the gravelled driveway to the Abbey. The congregation.

Kneeling and standing.

I lean back and stand, move a foot southwards towards the weak
English sun, pick another halved potato from the sack the old monk next
to me carries, and kneel again.

What's that you say, Brother Michael? Oh, nice and deep is right. I
am enjoying it, yes thank you. A cup of tea after Mass will be lovely. *A
cup of your weak dribbly tea. Earl Grey. Whoever the fuck he was.* We
will. Finish the length we're on and maybe stop then. Thank you
Brother.

Standing and kneeling.

Holding the next potato down. Drowning it in clay. In its grave. Or
its cradle. However you like to look at it. Whatever your outlook is.

Ah I don't know what's at me today. Apart from the generalities of
being here in this cold place and away from everything I knew and loved
and hated.

And the other thing that has been at me for thirty years.

Sometimes, when I think of what happened to me and what I did, I
want to throw my head back and howl.

A blackbird lands on the hawthorn tree at the side of the potato drill. I
look at it and he at me and for a second I am ten years old, home in
Ballyferriter, lurking behind Mr Nugent's hedge listening to the blackbird
that would land without fail when I was there. The local boys thought it
was hilarious when they heard me trying to copy the blackbird's singing.
Me with my unbroken voice. But the blackbird perched on Mr Nugent's
hedge liked it. Maybe he was taking the mickey out of me too when he'd
cock his head, look at me and wait till I'd finished before starting again.
But I don't think so. A proper duet we were. When word got out, I was
the laughing stock.

A bit odd, that fella, they said.

What're ya doing lurking behind Mr Nugent's hedge, my father said. You're to stop that ya amadán.

I didn't care. Michael Doherty was all GAA, John Foley would steal a handful of sweets from Devine's, Larry the Rock was necking beer from the taps of his parents' pub and Jonjo O'Neill we all knew was hanging around the convent, looking up hopefully at the posh boarding girls' windows, hands working in his trouser pockets.

I sang duets with a blackbird.

Then it all happened and my voice broke.

I hear a motorbike roar up the A-road a mile or two from the Abbey. Lonely sound. In the world outside, there is talk from America of the launch of a space shuttle, and it is the Queen's Silver Jubilee and Red Rum is winning all the races. But here, in the Abbey in the watery cold, it could be any time.

Brother Michael has taken a shine to me, the not-long-arrived gardener, and has sat me near the front of the church. I try and make myself small. 6 foot 2 I am and I crush myself down like a squeezebox. When they walk up the aisle – the brothers with their flowing skirts – Mrs Jones, her with the crippled boy, is in the gallery up behind attempting a top note. She doesn't get the ball over the bar. I turn and I swear that curly-haired priest grimaces.

New priest he is. Come in to say Mass for the Brothers. Handsome young fella he is. Not tall at all but a look of Robert de Niro off him. Clean and earnest. Like a newborn lamb. I catch the young one, Ivy Brown, blushing as he goes past, pretending to find the right page in her missal. He is turning from side to side, saying hello to people I suppose, and smiling. They are smiling back. Far cry from the church in Ballyferriter, you'd be killed there if you didn't look tragic the whole time. He reaches the front, turns and looks up at me.

Good morning he says.

His eyes are blue. There's kindness in them. I nod.

He turns back to the front, makes to go up the altar steps but trips and lands in a flurry of cloth. He tries to get up and his foot gets caught again in the surplice thing he has on and he collapses. He is flapping like a caught bird. The exposed sole of his right shoe seems profane. It's exciting like a road accident or the build up to a hanging. A boy in the row opposite sniggers and Mrs Williams gives him a clatter on the side of the head. No one is doing anything so I walk forward and offer my arm. The stupid man grabs it, rights himself and looks at me.

Up you get I say.

Deep blue his eyes are.

Go raibh maith agat he says.

For no reason I can fathom at all, a tear comes out of my eye.

When I think of what Jimmy and me did back on Coronation Day in 1953 I don't feel sorry.

If it was me myself it wouldn't have mattered. But Jimmy's people had nothing. And he was simple. Not the full shilling. He loved a laugh though and when Fr Butler was starting a drama group, Jimmy thought it would be great craic and it might get him close to the convent girls. Fr Butler, always full of airs and graces, decided that what Ballyferriter needed was some Agatha Christie. And Then There Were None was the name of it. Jimmy was playing a fella called Philip Lombard. Well, he thought he was the bee's knees.

My character is this, my character is that he said.

Swaggered around town he did and in and out of the Parochial House he went. Fr Butler ordered from Galway a fancy outfit for him and he had new shoes and for the first time in his life Jimmy was somebody. John Foley said he could borrow his bike any time he wanted and Jonjo O'Neill gave him the spare Beanos his father didn't sell in the paper shop.

I went up to him one day in the schoolyard.

How's rehearsals? Sure you have no time for us now you're a swank. He looked worried.

It's harder than you'd think.

But there was a vacancy to him. Like he was there but not there. I didn't say anything. I suppose I didn't know any better, I was only ten. And then word came that he had broken a window in the shed at the back of the presbytery. No-one knew why he would have been in the shed anyway but when Sergeant Morris got wind of it, Fr Butler said of course he didn't want to press charges, sure wasn't the boy under a lot of pressure with the part he was playing and didn't everyone know his father suffered from the drink?

When I heard they were looking for people to help move the bits of furniture on and off the stage in the parish hall I was excited. I ran to Jimmy's.

Don't do that he said.

Sure it'll be easy I said. We can have a laugh.

He looked at me strange. I volunteered anyway and when Fr Butler suggested I come round to the Parochial House to go over the props list, I thought nothing of it.

I won't go into what happened then and for the following year but let me just say that I have never taken my clothes off in front of any living creature since, and when, six years later, I smashed a big stone on top of Fr Butler's head, it was no more to me than swatting a fly, say, or putting a foaming dog out of its misery.

This blue-eyed English priest is apologising for his lateness, there has been a mix-up and the bishop has him covering two parishes, and he is saying that confessions will follow Mass instead of before. I don't know why he knows the Gaelic for 'Thank you'. Most people here are not interested in Ireland. They can't understand the neutrality in the war. I'd say read yer fucking history books but then I don't think those books mention anything about the Famine or 1916 or the colonisation or the endless crimes of this stupid country.

But there is something unusual about that priest. And familiar in some way.

The smell in a confession box is the same everywhere you go: dank and cold. Like an unused shed. I think of Jimmy one time when he came in at the same time as me when we were eight or nine. Messing like. Keeping his head below the grille. Tickling me until I couldn't help but laugh in Fr Ready's face. He threw us out and the waiting headscarved women and pious Pioneers were scandalised. Fr Butler was sent for.

Not to worry. Sure they're only children.

Only children. Fucking prick.

I wonder is there anything left of him? Does his skeleton still stand on the reservoir bed, ankles shackled with Jimmy's dad's spare fishing wire to a potato sack of stones? Bony arms swaying gently like a silent dancer? We burnt his clothes so they would not rise from the reservoir's bed with his body's decay and the rain that fell that night cleaned the waterside rocks nicely of his hectic blood.

The shutter flies back. Square of criss-crossed yellow.

Bless me Father, for I have sinned.

Same old rigmarole.

Ah hullo, you're the gardener aren't you?

I nod though I doubt he can see me.

It has been one month since my last Confession.

Yes?

And since then I took the Lord's name in vain and I was unkind in a letter home.

In what way unkind?

I was short with my cousin…she wanted me home for my father's funeral. I wouldn't go.

I see. He looks at me now directly and because he is lit though I am not, I see them clearly. My sister's eyes they're like. Yes.

Did you love your father?

I pause.

He was hard to love.

Silence.

Thanks awfully for helping me in the chapel. He smiles. You know I'm a priest for the past two years but I can't get used to the robes on steps and stairs. Stupid really.

I say nothing. He looks at me strange.

Do you mind me saying something to you? You might think as a priest I hear all sorts and of course I do, but really I just want people to be free and sometimes I think people don't say things in Confession because they don't trust me or they are ashamed or it's too difficult.

My knees are getting sore and I want to get out of there.

Please know I cannot be embarrassed. There is something on your mind, is there not?

I don't know what to say.

Earlier when you picked me up so kindly and I thanked you, you cried a little. Why is that?

I say nothing.

You know, the housekeeper in my school was Irish. She taught me 'Hullo' and 'Thank you' and such.

Right I say.

Is there anything at all you would like to say, anything on your mind?

My throat tightens and my chest heaves.

Please tell me.

Stupid tears are rising again. My sister's eyes he has. Something of the sea from home in them. And kind.

I'm a bit tired I say.

I thought you were.

Well…there is one thing, I say…

When I have finished, there is a long silence.

His voice is dispassionate, practical.

And are you sorry for what you did?

I remember something then. It was when we were stripping Butler's body after he had died. It took a while for the heart to stop even after he had finished breathing. We took off his watch, Jimmy kept that I think, and I went through his black trouser pockets and there was a card inside. One of those memorial cards and there was a picture on it. It was for a Margaret Butler. She was only a child. It must have been his sister. Why that stuck in my head for all these years I don't know but I remember it now and I remember now what I forgot then. That yer man, devil and all as he was, was a child once himself. And whatever he did to me, there was once a time when he hadn't done that thing to me.

So I say: At this minute I am. Yes, Father.

Where is Jimmy now? he asks.

There's no getting away from this young fella.

You can tell me.

I see Jimmy now as the last time I saw him, with his long beard, dirty mack, sitting on the Ballyferriter Main Street, bottle clutched like a child's teddy bear, shouting in unintelligible monosyllables at all who look in his direction. I see myself going the long way round so I would not have to look at him.

He died I say. Drink.

Although the confessional seal binds him and he cannot repeat what I have said, a bit of me wonders if a murder of a priest kind of overrides all that. I wonder what it would be like in a prison now. It's not a great time to be Irish here with the bombing and all.

He stares. I wait.

Do you sing? he says.

What?

I'm taking over the choir here when I come full-time. Will you give it a go?

I say nothing.

It helped me, he says. To clear some hurdles of my own.

His eyes are moist. I look at him and wonder.

A decade of the Rosary is all I get from him for penance. I wonder if there's been a mistake. Though I feel obliged to go to the feckin choir thing.

On Wednesday evenings there is practice. Fr Mansfield, for that is his name, gives me a sheet to sing from. I never tried to sing off a sheet with the notes on it before. Mrs Jones leans over.

When they go up, go up she says. When they go down, go down. That's what I do. Not always with great success. As you may have noticed.

Her breath smells sweet.

I help out now with her crippled son the odd time. I took him to a soccer match there not long ago. Don't think much of the game to be honest, not the skill of hurling, though I find myself kicking a stone down the street the next morning on my way to the Abbey. Mrs Jones and I have ended up bumping into each other a lot really. Fr Mansfield – I can't manage to call him Patrick as he asked – sometimes meets us for a cup of tea in Molly's Tea Shop in town. And though I still have not taken my clothes off in front of anyone, we went on a trip to the seaside in his Ford Escort there a while ago, the three of us, and I wore the shorts. Showed off the legs God help us.

After practice one night, Mr Hanby, the bank manager, pats me on the back.

What a wonderful voice. You're like John McCormack.

So now I am on the altar shaking like an eejit. The congregation is below. Fr Mansfield is looking at me encouragingly. I think of the blackbird behind Mr Nugent's hedge, of Jimmy's dopey laughter, of my sister and, yes, of that fucked up man who was once a boy, dead by my hand. They are all here now.

Fuck it I say under my breath. Fuck it all.

I throw my head up and sing.

DANIEL LAMBERT

Beckett in the Woods

My grandfather once told me he met Beckett in the woods. There were other people there when he told me, my mother and grandmother, but they left as he began to speak, and it was to me he was speaking.

'Beckett?' I asked. '*Samuel* Beckett, the writer?'

'Beckett the writer,' he said, 'Samuel Beckett, in the woods.'

I had been reading some of my father's books and had come across Beckett; mostly I had read his plays, but I knew he had written other things too.

'When was this?' I asked.

'Let me see,' he said, scrunching up his face and shuffling in his garden chair. 'How old are you?'

'Fourteen,' I said.

'Then it must have been about twelve years ago. God, it doesn't seem like yesterday ...' and he sat shaking his head.

Inside, through the kitchen window, I could see my mother, standing, watching us, pretending to dry a cup. She hated his stories; never once, as far as I had seen, had she sat through one.

'What was he doing in the woods?' I asked, still with one eye on her.

'He was crawling.'

'Crawling?'

'Crawling through the brambles. Like that character ... in that book of his ...'

He searched his mind, then looked to me, still thinking hard.

'I've only read that play, about the two men.' I said. 'And that other one, about the two other men. Sorry.'

'Never mind. But he was crawling, face down, on his stomach, clawing for purchase. Silly really: there was a path right next to him.'

'So, did you speak to him?'

'Of course I did. "You there," I said, "what on *earth* are you doing? Are you hurt? Do you need help?" Well ...'

At this, my grandfather shook his head, as if right back there and lost for words all over again.

'What did he say?'

'He said, "Don't worry, I'm quite fine." I asked him if he knew there was a path and he said he did. "I'm enjoying myself," that was his reply.'

I sat back myself then. He sat shaking his head, his eyes focussed on a point somewhere in the distance. I knew I must ask him one more question.

'How did you know it was Beckett?'

'Well,' he said, drawing his focus back to the garden, to me, 'he told me.'

When I asked her later why she was so angry about it, my mother refused to say much to me.

'It's all lies,' she said, filling the kettle with a bluster of water. 'It's always been the same with him.'

My grandfather had never been a literary man, not to my knowledge. If he was going to make up a story about meeting someone in the woods it would surely sooner have been a football player than an avant-garde playwright. I put this point to my mother and she shook her head.

'That man knows no limits.'

Later that night I leafed through a book of Beckett plays in the study.

My grandfather sat in the beer garden with a pint of amber ale and watched the starlings pass overhead as the sunset neared. We were, again, alone.

'When you saw Beckett,' I asked, 'did you know who he was at the time?'

He sat and sipped and looked up and seemed to be thinking.

'I'd heard of him, certainly,' he eventually said.

I nodded at this and left it at that. My mother then came from the pub, carrying a lemonade for me and a large glass of red wine for herself. It would normally have been smaller, but the death of her mother had apparently increased her thirst of an evening.

She sat and took a long drink – none of the sighting, smelling, swilling and sipping I'd seen on television – and sat staring into her own distance; different, I presume, from the distance her father was lost in. Her eyes were covered by large and expensive sunglasses.

'He told me he was writing a new novel,' my grandfather said, and I looked to my mother, wondering what her response may be. But I could see nothing through her sunglasses, and the rest of her face remained unmoved.

'Really?' I said, as casually as I could. 'What about?'

'He said he didn't know.'

My mother sighed.

The house was no more quiet with her gone. She had never been a noisy woman, or one who necessarily stood out much. It certainly felt different. But, looking around, it really wasn't that different; just that my grandfather was now sitting in my grandmother's old recliner, watching the cricket on the television.

My mother still didn't like going there – she hadn't liked it even when she lived there, or so she always said – and she always blamed that on her father. She had gone to check on him and I had said I would stay a while to keep him company. She left without saying in words how little she cared.

I sat on the other armchair and pretended to watch the cricket until I could be silent no longer.

'Did you just leave him there?'

'Who?' he asked, not turning from the screen.

'Beckett. Did you just leave him, in the brambles, or did he get out?'

Still watching the television, he seemed to be thinking.

'I think he stayed there,' he said.

'You think?'

'Yes.'

'Seems strange.'

'It *was* strange,' he said, confidently. 'It's not every day you see a man happily crawling through the brambles in the woods. He was wearing nice clothes too.'

I watched him. His dusty glasses resting on a crooked nose. Neatly shaven skin. Loosely combed hair. A pastel shirt. Black trousers. Old, navy blue slippers.

'Did you *really* see Samuel Beckett crawling through the woods?' I asked.

'I did,' he said.

She keeps telling me that he has no feelings. She brings it up every time there's even the slightest chance that it *could* be brought up; pulling it into arguments, or discussions disguised as arguments, where it doesn't seem even remotely relevant, let alone welcome.

'He was *always* making up stories. Elaborating on events. Stretching the truth. He never once remembered anything *I* did for him.'

The way she spoke made it sound like he was already dead.

The last time I spoke to him before he died we talked mostly about football. I didn't care much for it, but he did, and I liked to see him smile, even without his teeth in.

When my mother left the bedside to get a coffee from the café, I shuffled my chair a little closer.

'Did you *really* see him, in the woods?'

'Who?'

'Samuel Beckett.'

He lay back on the stiff hospital pillow and stared almost blankly up at the ceiling. His pale skin. His raw gums. That line of lighter skin on his left hand where his wedding ring had been until some five or so months ago.

Then he coughed.

'Can I have some water?' he asked.

I passed him the cup. He took a number of short sips and handed it back, his hand shaking.

'Thanks,' he said, gasping, shaking his head. 'Oh dear,' he said. 'Oh dear.'

He lay his head back and closed his eyes.

The next day, I went for a walk in the woods. I chose a path, walked it to the end. And then I went home.

CHETNA MAROO

Four Corners

There were three of us, all girls, all squash players, all undiscovered.

Whenever Amar and I were feeling gloomy about our bad luck, Pa would place his hands on our shoulders and tell us we must be patient. Immortality is no good for the young. That was how Ma would have put it, he told us. Amar's face went white when he said things like that. She wasn't angry, she was struggling with herself. She didn't want to offend him. Pa had formed the habit of leaning on Ma, of telling us what she would have said. But we didn't remember Ma like that. There were no proverbs or speeches. We remembered Ma's back, her shoulders, heaving under her blouse as she moved about the kitchen, a warm soapy forearm drifting out from time to time to keep us from harm. We remembered her fastening her red scarf over her head, her handbag bumping our arms when she brushed our cheeks with her fingertips – light as snowfall – before climbing the hill to work. Only rarely were there tentative snatches of enlightenment, things heard from movies and songs: *I'll be back; Don't break my heart*.

We felt bad for Pa. Neither of us contradicted him.

I was the youngest but Amar said that on court I was the wolf, because I was minded to play a long game. On top of that, she thought I needed the pack and would never leave my accustomed territory except when facing starvation. I wanted to agree and then add something of my own, maybe that Amar was the sun bear because she was so small and fierce. Or something about Rekha. I wanted to say that Rekha was the margay. It wasn't just her short neck. It was her ability to mimic speech to lure her prey. But only Amar could say things like that and make them sound pretty.

This day that I remember was in winter, when I was fourteen. It was a day that started and ended the same as most, and, really, nothing much happened, but nothing much was the same after.

At breakfast, Rekha was hissing at me across the kitchen table because she thought I had taken her old training shirt with '555' on the pocket. I told her it was Amar's shirt, which was true. Pa used to sew the numbers onto the pockets for all of us.

555 was the number of matches in the mighty Jahangir Khan's unbeaten run: 555 matches played without a single loss. There was no definitive record that would substantiate this number, but it didn't matter. It was sewn onto our pockets. Jahangir Khan was Pa's most beloved hero, but for Pa the number was a symbol of something greater than Jahangir himself. There was a whole dynasty behind him. We knew all along that we were nothing like the Khan family – even Pa knew – but he kept on sewing 555 onto our shirts, and then, when Rekha turned sixteen, the sewing stopped. I supposed Pa realized Rekha wasn't going to be a great player, and Amar said he had to treat us equally so he stopped for us, too.

Rekha grabbed at the shirt. I moved out of her reach. She leaned across the table, caught my wrist and began twisting it, hard, as if we were ten years old. I squawked. Amar got up, opened the fridge, shook up a two litre bottle of coke and pointed it at Rekha with her fingers ready on the lid. Things could escalate quickly once Amar got involved.

'This isn't your business,' Rekha said.

'It's my shirt,' Amar replied.

Rekha gave me hateful look. I could have shown her Amar's name on the label, but I didn't.

When Pa came into the kitchen, he noticed the shirt.

'There are men who built their game around beating a Khan,' he said, as he sat down next to me. He took up a knife, began slicing oranges, passing me the slices to pack in a Tupperware box. 'The good players ask themselves: What do I do if I come up against a Khan on the squash court?'

'We're not Khans,' Rekha murmured.

Pa's back straightened and his moustache seemed somehow to stiffen, but his eyes were lit up and beautiful when he looked at Rekha.

He said, 'We are brothers. Indians and Pakistanis.'

Rekha sniffed. She was ready for a fight. She wanted to say something cruel. Once, a long time ago, Rekha had caught Amar holding hands with a Pakistani boy outside the men's changing room and she told Pa, who spoke to the boy's mother, and as far as Pa and Rekha and the boy's mother knew, Amar never saw the boy again. But I knew that Amar met Sahir before school, or after tea when we went out to run.

I rubbed at my wrist and looked at Pa's face, wishing that Rekha would leave things alone. Rekha's neck became blotchy. Pa lowered his gaze, cut into the half an orange in his hand. Rekha opened her mouth and then, abruptly, with a beaten look, she closed it and slumped back in her chair.

That was when Amar got up. She kissed Pa's cheek and said, 'Tell us about Jahangir's father, Pa.'

Pa looked at her with such love in his eyes.

He said, 'Roshan Khan came to this country with five pounds in his pocket.'

'The same as you,' Amar said.

Pa kept slicing, smiling into his moustache.

And then he gave us his news.

'I'm bringing a man today,' he said. 'To watch you play.'

He winked at me, before fixing his attention on his hands that were working away at the oranges.

We all stopped what we were doing.

Amar touched my arm with her elbow. My cheeks grew hot. A month earlier, I'd gotten a wildcard into a challenger tournament. We both knew this man was coming for me.

Pa, still looking at his hands, sensed our reactions and he was happy. He passed me the last pieces of orange and wiped his fingers on a scrap of kitchen towel. Then he simply nodded and got up and left the room.

Rekha didn't hesitate. As soon as we heard the front door open and close, as soon as we felt the cold draft from outside, Rekha reached over, took a slice of orange from my box and announced that the man Pa spoke of was not a sponsor or a scout, but a suitor, for her or Amar. He would not be a Khan, she said. He would be a Chandaria or a Patel.

Amar had arranged to see Sahir and his friends that morning, but I wanted to talk to her about the scout.

'Tell him, no,' I pleaded, 'Tell him, tomorrow.'

She took my hand, pulled me along. 'Come, Kas. We'll talk on the bus.'

We could see them as we approached the football field. They were all standing around under the branches of the clump of trees at the edge of the pitch, eight or nine of them in big coats and boots. They weren't doing anything, just talking. The low sun lit the land all around them. One of the girls waved and we waved back.

Sahir broke away from the group.

'Fifteen minutes,' Amar told me, 'then we'll run for the bus and we'll talk.'

'Kas,' Sahir said. He looked at me when he said hi, like he was glad to see me. He lowered his head a bit. He smelled of good soap.

'Hey,' I said, and the two of them went off.

There was nothing much to Sahir, I thought, as they crossed the pitch. He walked with his head up like he knew about the world, and he was nice, and good-looking I supposed, but that was all. It didn't matter, because how could it last in any case, when our parent and his could never know? I dug at the ground with the edge of my boot.

'How's the game, Kas?' one of the girls said. She had long henna'd hair that she'd curled into big waves under her hat, and a tiny diamond stud in her nose.

'It's good,' I said.

The girl waited for me to say more, then gave me a nice smile, and turned to her neighbour.

I should have told her about the scout, about how it was a big thing, and what might happen if he wanted to see me again. Amar would have made something of that, or she would have asked the girl something in return, and she would have remembered the girl's name. The girl's diamond stud caught the light when she nodded or moved about.

I stood at the edge of the group, laughing when they laughed, but always a bit off, uncoordinated in some way, the same as on the school field. The park was big and open. The trees we stood under were the only ones. I moved in closer to the group. It seemed a long time before Amar and Sahir wandered back. They were holding hands, laughing, each wearing one of Sahir's big gloves, that were bronze-gold in the queer wintry light. They looked relaxed. They looked happy. Amar's face seemed different – at ease and startlingly clear, and, yes, happy. She looked over at me, smiled. I felt suddenly lonely. While Amar turned to greet Sahir's friends, I stared at the pitch that was mainly mud, and the dry, brownish grass in the distance. There was something about the barrenness of the land in this light, and the vastness of it, that was overwhelming. I pulled my hat low over my eyes.

Amar kept her promise to me. On the bus, she didn't talk about Sahir or his friends. She sat close in, and said, 'I knew Pa would bring someone for you.'

She was still wearing Sahir's big glove. We talked about my last tournament, about the man Pa was bringing.

When she fell silent, I knew her mind was on Sahir.

I looked down and murmured, 'Rekha said no-one would come.'

She didn't answer, just took my hand in her gloved one and looked out of the window, smiling. Her face looked like the face of a statue I'd seen once in a museum, a woman, two thousand years old, holding out a flower to the onlooker, and she – the statue woman – was smiling at something that we could never know anything about. That was how Amar looked, I thought. Maybe I didn't think it right then, maybe it was later.

Amar and Rekha were at each other's throats from the moment they took their positions on court. I had already beaten Rekha, while Amar had watched from the balcony. Now, Amar threw me the ghost of a smile through the court's glass back. While Rekha waited impatiently to serve, Amar gazed off into the distance. And then she opened out her little fist and, slowly, she began to wipe her sweaty racket hand along the side wall. The wall was dirty with round dark smudges from the balls that had glanced across its surface.

Rekha shuddered and lowered her racket. She drew her neck in. She couldn't help herself.

'We are not animals,' she hissed. 'Do you know how many men have gone before you, rubbing their sweat onto that –'

She knew it was no good, that Amar was only doing this thing – dragging her palm along the unwashed plaster – to goad her.

She served a typically weak lob into the middle of Amar's box. Amar volleyed it easily across the court into the nick. Then she managed a serve that had Amar's racket brushing the side wall, but she might as well have saved herself the trouble. Amar could beat Rekha with her left hand behind her back. Even I could. Rekha was taller and stronger than both of us, and nearly nineteen, but for all her talk of duty and discipline, when it came to the game, she didn't apply herself.

Later, when she was braiding my hair, sitting cross-legged on my bed, Amar would say that Rekha's favourite shot was a boast because talking to her was like watching a ball bounce off three walls before it reached you. She never said what she meant. For example, when Rekha said, 'Do you know how many men have gone before you, rubbing their sweat onto that...' she meant, 'You are going to have unprotected sex with a white man.'

Amar would tug really gently at my braids which felt nice and made me a bit dozy and she would talk about the game, and then Pa, and she would talk about Ma after that, mentioning the things she remembered. Only years later did it occur to me that she was doing it for me, so that those memories would become mine, because the first time we'd talked about Ma, I hadn't come up with anything.

After Rekha and Amar played, it was my turn. Rekha swiped the ball into the tin and walked out, dropping the racket into my hand while I was running in. I would have liked to run straight into a shot but I had to close the door, and as usual the metal latch stuck from the inside.

Amar waited while I snapped it back. Then she tapped her racket against mine and told me quietly, 'He'll come.'

I wanted to kiss her.

When it was Amar and I on court, we were happy. For both of us, it was the same: the two of us, the four corners and the T were all there was.

Amar let me warm up with a drill. She fed the ball long and high and I volleyed long and then moved back to boast my own volley. After a few rallies, we swapped sides. But it wasn't until we'd completed sprints and begun ghosting that I knew how I would feel about each of the four corners that day. Pa believed in ghosting, and so did I. When you moved with your racket, and without the ball, with speed and intent, again and again, it was more than a rehearsal. Sometimes I thought it was more than the game itself. Amar stood at the front, watching me while I ghosted ten shots at each corner and then ten volleys at each side of the T, moving back to the T after every ghost. When it went well, my body was weightless and it felt as if I was not of this world and yet I was in control. It was better than dancing. It was better than flying. When it went well, I imagined that I was both here and across the sea, in Cairo, alongside Amr Shabana.

Amr Shabana. His name was like breathing.

Rekha said that Pa was living in the past, that it was no longer all about the Pakistanis, but about the Egyptians, who played in glass courts at the foot of the pyramids. And I agreed with her. For all his grace and accuracy, I would have bet Jahangir Khan never ghosted as much as the Egyptians. I'd have bet he never ghosted half as much as Amr Shabana. That was the only way I could account for it. When it came to knowing his place on the court, Amr Shabana was the best. It was as though it was not only his mind, but his *bones* that were thinking. Other players thought with their blood. They wanted to move forward whatever the cost; they hit the ball too early. Amr Shabana would never sacrifice his own rhythm, his own body, for an ill-timed attack. That was what made him great.

I wondered if Amr Shabana ever feared a corner.

There were days when I knew that one corner would seem to close in on me and when it came to playing I would have to dig in and, even so, I would stumble. My upper body would seem awkward, I would misjudge my position and find my racket head striking the back wall, the side wall, unable to dig the ball out.

But that day, with Amar watching from the front of the court, I felt good in all four corners. I felt light on the T. I turned and lunged and there was a good pulse in my body. My racket was up. I knew my place. And when Amar and I played, it was the same. After a half hour, I was sweating terribly, but there was no tiredness in my legs. Behind us, we could feel that Pa had arrived. He was watching our game. We felt the shadow of someone beside him. My heart beat so hard, I wanted to shout. But I couldn't think about it, I couldn't think about anything. I had simply to keep going. Amar could hit the nick like an Egyptian, but that day it was me. Every shot was good and when I didn't get to the ball, that was fine too because I was moving effortlessly and, when I needed to, I was exploding out of the T. Amar was glad for me. She was helping me, pushing me, making me excel.

And then, all of a sudden, I felt a change in Amar. Her racket head dropped, as if there was no more to do. I turned, instinctively, to Pa. He was alone. There was no-one else. He looked as though he had been standing there like that a long time. I wondered if I had imagined the man beside him. I wondered where Rekha had gone. Pa raised a hand. He looked ashamed. He said he'd be back soon and moved off, along the corridor, towards the bar.

Soon, Rekha appeared.

'No-one came,' she said. She'd been checking the guest book.

Amar snapped the latch on the door and we stepped out into the corridor, took up our towels to wipe our faces and under our arms. Neither of us acknowledged her.

I didn't know what made her do it right then, when Amar and I were worn out and dejected, but Rekha began to give a speech in front of the benches outside the courts.

'You two, you have decided I'm no good,' she murmured. 'You've made up your minds. You think I'm filled with sanctimonious thoughts. You think bad things about me because you want them to be true.' She hesitated, and then she said, as if this was the worst thing of all, 'You think I do not see it.'

It was just like Rekha to act like a martyr, to set herself apart from us. I dropped my towel and stared at her. She wasn't looking at me; she was looking at Amar, whose eyes were lowered. I could tell Amar was actually ashamed and didn't know what to say. And then I felt the same way. The floor seemed to move a little. I closed my mouth. Rekha was right. We had made up our minds about her.

Rekha should have left things there, but she didn't. She kept on going. Her voice shook.

'It isn't me you should be worrying about,' She looked at Amar. 'You're not a baby. Running around with Sahir like it doesn't matter, like no-one will ever find out. And you, Kas.' She stopped to make sure I was listening and then she said, slowly, *This is not all there is.*'

She waved a hand above our heads, indicating the two glass-backed courts where we had played every day since we could hold a racket.

Amar's face was white. I grabbed my kit bag, dug around for a roll of yellow tape and dropped down on the far bench, where I began taping my grip.

When Pa came, he knew something had gone on. He lifted a hand briefly to Rekha's cheek, then rested the hand on Amar's shoulder.

'You played well,' he said. His voice was loud. He was looking at me, but I kept on winding my tape. Pa lowered his voice. 'He was watching from the balcony, Kas.'

I could tell that Amar was relieved, though she was still pale, and I too was glad he had said that. Pa's face was tired, but it was proud and serious. His moustache was trimmed, dark, like a soldier's. He was the most handsome man I had ever seen.

While Amar went upstairs with Pa to pay for our court, Rekha and I changed our shirts and then sat on the bench looking into the court in silence. Its white walls seemed in poor shape, and so did the red service line and the red lines marking the service boxes and the out line. Pa had promised me that in the summer, I would take a job cleaning and painting the courts, and with the money I would get a new racket. The thought of it had buoyed me up, but now there was only a weak, sickly feeling.

They took a long time paying, and when they came back, Amar touched my shoulder and Pa put out a hand for me. I slid my racket into my bag and got up. The four of us began walking out and Pa's arms were around all our shoulders.

Amar was walking lightly, happily. Her cheeks were flushed a deep pink. She whispered, soft as anything, into my ear, 'Pa is good,' as if it had been in doubt. I looked at her cheeks, and the way her eyes were shining and I knew that while they were upstairs, and we were waiting on the bench, she had told Pa about Sahir, and she had said it easily and made him see that she was certain about it, and he had nodded, allowing it.

Maybe I should have told her that I was glad and I loved her, but I kept thinking of the muddy pitch and the dry grass that went on forever and I couldn't speak. I *was* glad. She pressed my hand, or maybe I pressed hers.

Outside, it was still light, and it was cold. There was an orange glow all over the car park. I felt the first touch of snow on my cheek.

'I forgot something,' I said. 'My tape.'

They went on to the car while I sprinted back.

Inside, I grabbed my racket and dropped the bag as I ran onto the court, leaving the door unlatched. There, on the T, I could breathe. From the other court came the echoing sound of the ball, hit cleanly and hard. My eyes were closed, my racket head was up. Pa had told us that when we prepared to ghost, we must clear our minds. But this time, I didn't. This time, I held in my head the four walls, the corners, the red lines, and then I saw the light on the football pitch, the light on Amar's face with her two-thousand-year-old smile, and all that mud and grass that went on and on.

With my eyes still closed, I began.

Forehand drop, T, backhand drop, T, forehand drive, T, backhand drive, T, volley –

CORRINA O'BEIRNE

Variation of Molly

Sunday 24th September

11p.m. Dominic, or the purveyor of lies as I now think of him, left me three weeks ago. No warning signs. No argument or chance to talk things over. Just a scribbled note. That's our goodbye. What kills me is Dominic spends a fortune on bespoke stationery, Mont Blanc pens, Japanese stamp blocks, high grade paper from a tiny paper mill in Strasbourg. All about the high opacity, apparently.

I'm not worth a sheet though. This was chicken-scratch on the back of our electricity bill:

Poll,
I'm sorry –
I'll arrange a time to pick up the rest of my vinyl.
D.
Ps. You can keep Mr Woo, Gabriella's putting me up for a few weeks and she's allergic to cats.

Thirty-five words. A couple of full stops, the odd comma, a pointless dash.

Gabriella.

She's Assistant Designer at his company: LOCO CREATIVE. Portuguese. Thin as a rasher of wind. I should have known something was going on by the way Dominic rolled her name around in his mouth like he could taste the letters…every juicy vowel, every syrupy consonant.

Gabrie*llll*a.

I've met her. All five-foot nine inches of her. Quite pretty, if you go in for that really obvious kind of beauty. He brought her to our flat once after LOCO CREATIVE's quarterly SAUCE MONSTER BASH. Which is essentially an all-you-can-drink affair that runs for three days. He brought her *here*, to our flat. They were both soaked to the skin with booze and God knows what else. She was wearing a sheet of gauzy white organza, held in place by a gold bodice. Adidas trainers. Gazelles. Coral pink, boxfresh. And an enamel brooch – a dark red heart with an orange lightning bolt cutting through it.

She was pretty. Yes, pretty. Dark skin, blue eyes, effortless hair. Beautiful, striking actually.

Dominic was hanging off her like a necklace. He kept stamping his feet, poking my side, like a toddler.

Starving. Me starving. Feed me!

I made them a Spanish omelette. Cut it into cubes, speared them with some leftover cocktail sticks.

'It's not that exciting, Gabriella,' I said, 'but hopefully it will remind you of home.'

Dominic nearly died of laughter, 'She's Portuguese, Polly. *POR-cha-gal*. Different countries, yeah? Told you she was a bit clownish, Gab!'

They both looked at my slippers, half-tried to suppress a laugh. She didn't laugh quite as loudly as he did. She caught my eye and her laugh turned into something else. I don't know, a pity smile? The kind of look I give the homeless guy outside of Marks and Spencer.

Another time, she turned up to his birthday party with some of her vapid *leggy* friends, bouncing their bulbous bums all over the place. I've never seen make-up like it – the kind of girls that see their actual face as just a light suggestion. I wanted to go over to them and say: *Calm down darlings, it's your face, not a colouring book*. He was all over me. Public displays of affection are...*were*...very *un*Dom. He would never hold my hand in public. I put it down to him being drunk – but no, he was using me, his girlfriend...his pathetic, loyal girlfriend, to fire his Portuguese lover up. I found her crying in the toilets. I blotted away her running mascara. I can't believe she had the audacity to let me comfort her.

De Moura.

Gabriella De Moura.

I bet he loves having a girlfriend with an exotic name.

Monday 2nd October
8.p.m. She's given me 48 hours. Clarissa, she's given me 48 hours. I was summoned to her massive corner office this morning. I'm to use the time to reflect on whether I genuinely think my position at Mustoe, Shorter and Mustoe is in any way tenable in light of my outburst at our Twickenham away day. Outburst? She's overreacting – we'd all had too much to drink.

'I've been here for five years,' I said. 'I'm a good paralegal.'

'That doesn't give you the right to call our Vice-Chairman a 'geriatric shit-pouch''.

'I've apologised,' I said. 'And I really am very sorry.'

'Apologies are pointless,' she said icily, head cocked, keyboard clacking.

I said someone may have spiked my drink. I'm not saying they did and I wouldn't want to take MSM down that avenue...That's when she brought out her trump card, which I wasn't prepared for. She produced an oversized envelope from her drawer with a theatrical flourish.

'This is your browsing history over the last fortnight. Would you like me to select a few highlights?'

I tried to find some kind of inner-poise, but it felt like someone was knitting in my stomach. 'Not especially,' I said.

'Needless to say, your web activity completely violates MSM's IT policy. It also raises concerns about the state of your mental health. You're a very angry person, aren't you?'

I gabbled a little. Made a few silly allegations. Tried to stall for time so that I could object properly and intelligently.

'Polly,' she said, holding both my wrists. 'Please don't force me to get Martin from HR up. Be smart. Read between the lines – a gracious exit, without fuss. You've got 48 hours to reflect on my offer; I suggest you take it.'

Wednesday 4th October
Went for a walk in Clarence Park. Autumn is a bully. Yanking at trees. Everything butchered.

Thursday 5th October
9.30a.m. I spoke to Dominic. Well, left a voicemail. Only to see if he wants to collect his vinyl. And to tell him about MSM. Don't ask me why, but I feel like he has a right to know I'm soon to be unemployed. If he wants to talk, to offer me an explanation, an apology, I wouldn't be closed to that.

6.15p.m. Found Dominic's old suede swagger-coat in a bin liner under the stairs. We thought it got lost in the move. Deep chocolate with a silk cream lining. Cigarette burn still on the cuff (not sure where I thought it might have gone?). I put my face into the butter-coloured faux fur collar – the smell of the basement at The Roxbury on a Friday night – smoky and sweet, like a cinnamon cigarette.

He loved that coat, I loved that coat.

I wrapped it around myself. Watched *Cash in the Attic*. How it ever got commissioned is beyond me.

11.30p.m. Gabrie*llllllllllllla*. Gabriella De Moura. I looked it up online. It means 'Heroine of God'. Well how lovely for her. Do you know what

Polly means? Nothing. It means nothing. Just a variation of Molly. Figures.

Saturday 7th October

My favourite band ever is The Smiths. They are the musical equivalent of crystal meth. Dom bought me *Meat is Murder* for our three-month anniversary. July 2003.

'Songs are like tattoos,' he said. 'That was Joni Mitchell, I can't take credit. But I'm giving you your first tattoo, Poll and I take full credit for that.' He could take all the credit he wanted as far as I was concerned. Spend that credit however he chose.

People don't believe me when I say they are the only band I ever listen to but it's true. There's more genius, poetry, meaning in their song titles than any other band can fit into an entire album.

Track 6. 'How Soon is Now?'

I am the son
And the heir
Of a shyness that is criminally vulgar

The tragedy of loneliness. It was like being skinned alive by beauty. Morrissey and Marr at the peak of their powers, interlacing perfectly. My mind was cracked open, right there in Dom's bedroom. I cried. I cried because it was the first present he'd given me. I cried because it was so harshly beautiful and because I knew I could wait a whole lifetime for a moment like that to be repeated. The swampy guitar intro that makes you feel like you're spinning, the clanging bells, tremolo-and-slide soundbed. Morrissey…looping around me, trapped like fog between my ears:

You shut your mouth
How can you say
I go about things the wrong way?
I am human and I need…

Endless, endless echoes.

'Don't let me fall in love with you,' I said.

'I won't,' he said. Mouth/mouth, heartbeat/heartbeat. 'I won't.'

Monday 9th October

If someone I loved as much as Dominic thought I wasn't worth being with, then I don't want to be with me either. So where does that leave me? Where, exactly, do I go from here? People ask me: what do you need? I need for him not to be gone. But they can't help with that. Their pupils go wide, and they stare at their feet, embarrassed.

I haven't cried. People encourage it, they say it's cathartic. Like, if I sit down and have a good weep – all the pain, the anger, will roll off my back. So today, I pulled the curtains and I urged myself to cry. Nothing. What does that say about me?

Thursday 12th October
Segment on *This Morning* about fusion food. Dom was such a sucker for it, he was only interested in combinations of food that shouldn't go together. Pad Thai Taco. Sushi pizza. Bacon infused doughnuts.

I always made out that I thought it was culinary witchcraft, but the truth is I couldn't take it seriously. Vegetables embroiled in an identity crisis – since when is grated cauliflower, rice? It needs to be smothered in cheese sauce and cooked at 180 for forty minutes.

Once, we went to this restaurant in Herne Hill that served root vegetable chips on a mini-washing line. The line was edible, the chips were cut into t-shirt shapes. I tried to take it all in my stride, but inside I was dying, I felt so self-conscious.

Cow's milk was too obvious, so Dominic switched us to nut milk (I didn't have the heart to point out that almonds don't have teats). And for the last year of our relationship he plunged, head-first, into the whole 'food that isn't there' craze…where chefs bulldoze through the actual structure of the actual food. Foam (usually mint or basil). Raspberry dust. Parmesan air. A distant memory of broccoli. A threat of pork.

2 a.m. I tried to watch *Newsnight*. It was Emily Maitlis interviewing Emma Thompson about sexual harassment in Hollywood. I can't bear the way she struts about the place. So sure of herself (EM not ET). All monochrome mini-skirts and plunging necklines. She looks like she's ready for a night out, not fronting a serious current affairs show. A few weeks ago, she was talking about allegations of torture somewhere (Libya?) and she's perched on the desk, swinging her legs all over the studio. She wants a spot on *Strictly Come Dancing*.

Sunday 15th October
That baby next door is crying for my benefit, a constant reminder that I'm light years away from becoming a mother. Let's face it, I've had an implant under my arm so long I'm probably sterile, clean out of eggs. Some women ooze it…you just know they're dangerously fertile. I'm not talking about the obvious ones that are always pregnant – Kirsty Allsopp or Ella from MSM accounts. You see them, on the street – you think WOW you are a walking bag of ovaries. If you wake up one

morning and decide you're going to get pregnant, by midday you'll be lactating.

There was that one time. The wrong time. Before the launch of LOCO CREATIVE.

Tuesday 17th October
I'm friends with Gabriella on Facebook. Set up a fake profile: Imogen Bexley. She's younger than me, a freelance illustrator, highly developed thigh-gap, a social butterfly. Bit of a female Phileas Fogg. It was easy, I copied lots of photos from Photobucket and created a collection of travel albums. Most recently, Imogen's been to Peru. Inca Trail. Sacsayhuaman. Cerro Colorado Vinicunca.

I played it smart. First, I built up a friend base. I just sent out hundreds of friend requests: accepted, accepted, accepted! Then I scanned through Gabriella's friend list, selected those with over 500 friends. No-one has that many friends; clearly, they'll accept anyone to keep their numbers up. I got about five or six in the bag, including her best friend, Jemima (a nutritionist) then added Gabriella. I didn't have to wait long, she accepted within fifty minutes.

Her mother is beautiful. Beautiful in way that is beyond description. She looks like Isabella Rossellini. So much so that I googled her (Isabella) to see if she has any children. She does: a daughter, Elettra and an adopted son, Roberto.

Thursday 19th October
Slept until 2 p.m. today, felt like waking from a coma. MSM couriered over the contents of my desk. No 'Sorry you're leaving!' card or token gift or letter from Clarissa. Even the interns get an Amazon voucher. What a sad legacy! An unopened blister pack of magnesium supplements. A self-help book from Joanna, smug looking bloke on the inside cover, shit-eating grin. Teeth so white they could be battery-powered.

Cancelled all my subscriptions. *Private Eye. The Economist. New Statesman.* It's not like I ever read them. No one reads them, you only ever skim-read the occasional article. I'd fan them out on my desk to impress Clarissa. Every few weeks she'd thumb through *Private Eye*, tell me she'd like to ruin Ian Hislop and saunter off.

11p.m. Just brushed my teeth and caught sight of my face in the mirror. I've avoided my reflection since he left. Before I could do anything, there I was. Pale. Weak. Barely conscious. Like a blood donor who couldn't say no.

Friday 20th October
Called Dominic this afternoon. Straight to voicemail. I told him we need to talk – because (call me old-fashioned) when you've been in a relationship for fourteen years you owe the other person an hour of your time. He's got a double-first from Bristol, for Christ's sake, he knows he can't behave like this.

6.45 p.m. Bought 300g of mixed mushrooms. Oyster. Shiitake. Cremini. For a stroganoff that didn't happen. I've ordered some Vietnamese and I'm going to get an early night.

3 a.m. The world is vastly overpopulated. By the time I'm 70, there will be 9.7 billion people. BILLION! These are *medium* estimates by a world-renowned Data Scientist living out of shoe-box in Arizona. The world adds 80 million a year, that's the population of Germany. Wake up, everyone! There isn't enough world to fit us all in, we don't have enough water as it is.

This isn't junk science, this is real. I've been living with my eyes shut. I read something about a vacuum bubble, which I didn't understand but it didn't sound good. The universe is unstable, destined to fall apart.

Most of us will starve to death. Goodnight and good luck people.

Saturday 21st October
They're in Barcelona. Status update from Gabriella this morning. I asked him to take me a thousand times, but he was always too busy with LOCO CREATIVE. They're packing everything in: La Pedrera, Park Guell, La Rambla. There's this cringey photo of them leaning against the Sagrada Família like it's a garden wall. She's obviously turned him into one of these metrosexual types, he looks like a circa 1972 David Bowie wannabe.

11 p.m. Imogen posted her first ever status update on Facebook. Well, a quote:

"Life becomes easier when you learn to accept an apology you never got." Six likes.

Sunday 22nd October

Today, I shared a slice of toast (skinny white Danish Bread=tracing paper) with Mr Woo and fell asleep on the sofa. That's me all day. I'm embarrassed at how pathetic I am. How can I be surprised he walked away? I want to walk away from me too.

3 a.m. The things you notice when you're constantly in the flat. The humming of the fridge, fuzzy static of appliances, the stench of bleach (where?), the soft applause of the cat-flap.

Sensible people never win, do they? I mean, look at me. Being sensible hasn't got me anywhere. I'm so sick. I'm so sick of myself.

P.S. It's me. Late. Does love count if it's one-sided? Do you have to have had love to lose it? LOSTLOVELOST. You let me believe we were fine, Dominic. You did that. Well, fuck you for not being honest.

Monday 23rd October

Penguins mate for life. And seahorses. I read it on the internet. If a seahorse can be monogamous, why can't a man? Can anyone answer me that because I really would like to know.

It's pretty upsetting when you think about it. It's not like I expected the world. Nothing spectacular, nothing excessive. Just a quiet, steady love.

I called my sister.

I don't know why I do it to myself, it's like self-flagellation. Joanna's going to do Veganuary which means she knows everything about how the world works. Oh, and she's a digital activist. Online petitions. Someone needs to tell her that clicking 'send' doesn't really count. Every social movement she signs up to is being meticulously monitored and analysed so she's basically backing the marketisation of social change. And for someone who is so bloody concerned with what is happening on a global scale she is completely unhindered by empathy on matters closer to home.

She's a crap sister.

I'm not meant to say that. I'm meant to say she's my best friend. And I'm totally in love with my nephew. I adore his Lego haircut and I don't find him deeply patronising. I'm meant to say that I love my brother-in-law (a self-proclaimed recovering narcissist) as if he were my actual brother.

Joanna hasn't come to see me since he left. Aren't sisters, meant to...be there? Shouldn't she have turned up at my door? Bottle of wine in hand? Force me to burn photographs of him/us. Mum hasn't turned up either. Ok, now I feel bad. Mum's just had a double mastectomy.

No. I can't. I can't write…I can't write it.

Why do I feel like, if it were Joanna…if Marcus had left Joanna, Mum would…somehow …find the strength to get out of her dressing gown and on the train?

Joanna told me I'm still in love with Dominic. I denied it, I don't know what I am.

'Don't throw yourself away because he doesn't want you.'

'Look, will you please shut up?' Silence. Awful silence. Swollen and swelling.

'What did you say? How dare you speak to me like that?'

'I can't just erase him.'

'Wake up, Polly! He's been slowly stripping your relationship down for parts. You said that yourself.'

'I didn't say that.'

'Christmas last year. You were drunk. Sisterly chat.'

I said I didn't remember.

'Ok, then I'm lying. I'm not remotely surprised he's gone.'

'I'm sorry you find my heartache so dull.'

Oh, she didn't like that. She didn't like that one bit.

'Jesus, my nerves have a limit. I've got my own plate of shit to eat today thank you very much.' This has been her phrase of choice throughout 2017.

She was still shouting at me as I put the phone down. I don't remember leaving the house or running down Chester Road.

Stop being a victim.

Were they Joanna's words or mine? It didn't matter. I was going to even up the score.

Down Poynter Road, up Highgate. I looked at my feet – one New Balance, one Saucony. I ran until I could hardly breathe, just ragged gasps. The urgent rumble of wheels – thrumming in my teeth. My heart in my ears. People twisted out of my way, a sponge-faced old lady asked me if I was ok. *No,* I wanted to scream, *No, no, no. I'm not bloody ok.* But you can't speak to strangers like that, can you?

I raced out of BUTCHTOPIA, brown parcel in hand. Adrenalin fizzed through my blood.

I punched their door. Arms swinging, like I wanted to knock it out.

I'm here, I screamed, *you will deal with me now.*

I wanted him to see what he's done to me, dare him to look me in the eye. I punched their door again and again and the words kept coming and coming, until they weren't really words and my voice turned to water.

I didn't care. Even if the blinds were drawn and they were sitting in their living room staring me dead in the face, I still would have done it. I ripped open the brown parcel and shoved them through their shiny letterbox.

Got home around 8.p.m. Soaked my mangled knuckles in a bowl of ice-water and I opened a bottle of vodka. It tasted hot and clean. Toasted a few memories and drank…and drank until I felt peaceful…weightless…. like swimming under water. It was transcendent.

Monday 23rd October
It's all unfolding on Facebook, Gabriella's status is an absolute joy.
Welcome to the neighbourhood…pigs trotters through the door!
The inevitable flurry of activity ensued. We're at a grand total of forty-seven comments:

DesPIGable!
That's snout nice. Sow uncool!
Should have set up house in Belgravia!
You and Dom coming to ours on Wednesday? Inbox me beautiful!

You like little surprises, Gab? That's good to know.

Tuesday 24th October
I got up early and went for a walk around Clarence Park. Crunching leaves, crisp air. Every shade you can think of: scarlet, saffron, copper, gold. Everything just…letting go. I would be ok, I told myself. I could edit him out of my life. I would write a new one, a new life. It would take time, but I would do it. Edit. Him. Out.

I tried not to think of him, I really did. But I didn't get past five minutes. He was everywhere.

In the coffee van queue.

In the playpark.

His face…his smell…like sun warmed grass. I thought about holding my breath…

I didn't want it in my lungs…but I could feel it coating my jacket, my hair and I let it fill my nose a little…I felt myself disappear into the memory of his body…delicate fluttering in my stomach…like being dive-bombed by butterflies.

Friday 27th October
When I think of all the things I haven't done it makes me feel physically sick. I'm thirty-six and I haven't read a single piece of Greek mythology.

Everyone I know has accomplished some kind of physical challenge – ice-climbing Ben Nevis was a big thing last year. And shouldn't I have been somewhere by now? Somewhere that counts, that would say something about the kind of woman I am? I haven't travelled further than Croatia.

I'm going to do something about it. Right now. I will peel off my old skin like a coat – a new Polly Clarke will be born. No fixed parameters, anything goes...

Obtain an actual marketable skill.

Start taking magnesium (stick with it this time!)

Watch *Breaking Bad* and/or *Orange Is the New Black* (Dom refused = too mainstream)

Australia. Bora Bora? Easter Island.

I lack presence (solution?)

Boston marathon.

5 p.m. It's basically impossible to ignore your phone when it's buzzing. I figured that if I didn't look, it would probably ruin my evening and distract me from finishing my 'me' list, because I'd be wondering who it was. And I wanted to focus all my energy on writing my list.

A status update from Gabriella. *Our long-awaited engagement party is here. Champagne central.* Ninety-eight likes.

The love I wasted on that man. My blood curdled.

Late thirties. Lemon yellow hair flowing behind her like a flag. An enormous brown dog on a metal chain. A Great Dane or a German Shephard. I don't know what breed it was, but it was big. I knew what she was up to. That's the thing with people around here. They flounce around in their Tom shoes, sipping their coconut masala chais, with their backpacks made of landfill, harping on about territorial emissions (it's all so paint by numbers). But – here's the thing – if you aren't standing right next to them while their dog turns itself inside out, they'll pretend they haven't noticed. And that mutt left a steaming mound of the stuff. I asked a passer-by for a bag and without giving myself time to think better of it, I scooped it up. That's what he's reduced me to – picking up poo in the park.

I spent the rest of my weekend imagining how they'd arrive home, push open the front door and slip straight through that shit-mountain. Or even better, they've been away for the weekend and left the heating on, so it would essentially be cooked and there'd be flies and maggots. Dominic never could deal with anything messy and I'm sure the Heroine of Love would refuse to deal with it. By my estimations a good professional cleaning company in their area would charge at least £170 plus there's the embarrassment factor. Imagine explaining to the cleaner, 'Yes, we came home to find someone had posted dog poo through our letterbox.' It says a lot about the kind of people they are.

It's my engagement present to the happy couple.

10 p.m. I burn with loneliness. He'll take some responsibility for that. He'll take some responsibility for the fact that he flat out refused to ever be completely mine but made me his. He'll take responsibility for the fact that living with him was a form of perpetual torture – never quite like being alone but never quite like being with another person either, it was somewhere – horrible – in-between. How for the last three years of our relationship I was basically used in the same way everyone else uses a smartphone. I became his substitute brain, extra storage space to remember birthdays, set reminders, organise finances. All outsourced to The Variation of Molly.

At least I had the guts to fall in love. I see the truth of who he is now. A bag of shit through his door does not make us even. We are not square.

Zero from Gabriella on Facebook. No status update about *that* gift.

5th November
I don't normally go out on Bonfire Night because the bangs scare Mr Woo but I found myself drifting over towards the park. The evening sky glowed with streaks of fierce pink. A group of women were erecting an effigy - a huge Harvey Weinstein, standing on the base of an Oscar award, a Hollywood Star hanging from his forked black tongue, a clapperboard emblazoned with the words FINAL CU[N]T smashed into his saggy genitals. The countdown begun...*10...9...8*

...two bobble-hatted girls skipped by, trying to write their name in the air with sparklers....*3...2*

...*1*. Fireworks climbed the sky, slashes of green and red stunned the ground. The air was heavy with smoke and anticipation. *LIGHT HIM UP! LIGHT HIM UP!* I'm not a fan of collective enthusiasm, but I went with it. Flames tore into his legs. A stranger high-fived me and we smiled.

A sudden wind slapped my face.

There was this guy, selling fireworks. Molotov Cocktails. Aerial Shells.

'If you want to put on a show, these are the way to go!' he said. 'She'll shoot through the air like a missile.'

Tomahawks he called them. £40. Each. Crappy plastic lighter – £3.50.

There'd be some damage. Fireworks are dangerous, indiscriminate. They'll take out whatever is in their path. We're warned about that from an early age – be careful.

I didn't have a fixed idea about how things would turn out. That's something I've learnt over the last few months: don't plan, don't map things out.

It would be an impressive display. A coruscating kaleidoscope of every imaginable colour. Pink. Green. Indigo. It would generate some heat, confusion, fear. In a confined space? Walls. Doors. Ceilings. They all scream ricochet.

First maybe a lamp gets smashed, their parquet flooring might get ripped open. Some photographs or a vase would get nuked.

But that Tomahawk would find them. It would cut through their skin like hot butter.

Slice off a digit. Burrow into a face…an orbital blowout fracture or something simple like a nice gaping hole. Like I say, I didn't have a fixed idea. Karma has no menu, after all. You get served what you deserve.

I had every intention of going through with it. I traced the nose of the Tomahawk around their letterbox. I could light the fuse, hurl it through and disappear around the corner in less than ten seconds. I could taste hot metal in my mouth. Jazz-like bursts of screeching and hysterical laughter in the distance. I began to laugh, to join in with the distant hysterics. I laughed until there was no sound.

No. What was I thinking? A firework? Through their letterbox?

He took fourteen years from me. Thousands of days, stolen. Gone. Never to berecaptured. You don't get to do that to another person. I'm a paralegal, I know about the importance of justice, of cause and effect.

A firework. Where's the creativity in that? Oh, I can do a lot better. Because I'm not broken anymore. There's nothing left in my heart to break.

I know he would like me to become smaller, fade to a pinprick. Die, even? That would be neater. He needs to know that isn't going to happen. Yes, most days I am pathetic, I know that. Most days I feel so insignificant that I am barely an *ism*. But some days, at the edges, I feel like there is more of me than I ever imagined. I am inflating – no morphing – no blossoming – no – it doesn't matter, what matters is that I like it. I like it and that scares me. It should scare him.

I'm flicking my light back on.

He doesn't get to walk away from me unscathed, unpunctured, un-fucking-anything. He may think he is free of me, but he's not. He's not free of me.

RYAN O'CONNOR

Ouroboros

I was standing in line waiting on a bus when I noticed someone had scratched, *all journeys are lies*, into the lamppost I was leaning against. My father was in hospital back home and I was on my way to visit him, but when I read that I stepped out of the queue and walked away. I'd left my hometown almost twenty years before and hadn't been back since. It had been longer since my father was last home.

News of his return was relayed in two voicemails my sister left in the space of five minutes. In the first she said he'd turned up unannounced on her doorstep. In the second, after a silence that seemed to deform the space and time around her words, she said he'd been admitted to hospital and that he was terminally ill and didn't have long to live.

Directly opposite the bus station on the other side of the street there was an off-licence. I crossed the road and stood looking in through the window. It wasn't part of a chain or somewhere you'd go to buy an expensive bottle of wine. The window was overcrowded with large star shaped fluorescent price cards and green and red neon signs advertising beers and wishing you a *Merry Christmas* three hundred and sixty-five days a year, while inside there was a metal grill to protect the staff from the customers. In the window display a golden Maneki-neko, its raised left paw swinging in a continual beckoning gesture, sat in a little wooden rowing boat amid a sea of bottles. Someone else must have stood where I was now watching it beckon them too, because they'd written *not waving but drinking :)* with a black marker on the windowpane.

When I entered, the shop assistant looked up from his newspaper and watched me peer through the metal grill and study all the different bottles on the shelves. There were so many I didn't know which one to choose. For a while I stood there looking at them like I was gazing at the stars or trying to figure out a complex equation on a school blackboard. Eventually the guy put his paper down and approached me.

'What are you after?' He asked, looking at me and then back at the bottles, like he was going to formally introduce me to whichever one I chose.

'I don't know,' I told him.

'What do you normally drink?'

'Whatever does the job.'

'What job?'

'Takes me where I need to go.'

'Where's that?'

'Today, to see my father.'

I don't know when I started mixing alcohol with alchemy, conflating one thing with the other. Where I got the idea that there were certain drinks for certain occasions or tasks. Every addict knows that in the end it all does the same thing, leads you to your very own hell. Still, every time I stood in an off-licence or in front of a gantry in a bar, insight went out the window and I'd tell myself this time might be different. Ignoring the years of self-inflicted wounds, the near-death experiences, I kept searching for that magic bullet and playing Russian roulette with the bottle. Believing if I chose correctly, the next drink might provide the click that blew all the shit out of my head, wiped my mind clean, and lead me to salvation. Maybe it wasn't such an unusual thing to do – Carl Jung once remarked that *alcohol* in Latin is *spiritus*, and that we use the same word for the highest religious experience as well as for the most depraving poison.

'Whisky, I'll take a bottle of whisky,' I told him.

'A malt?'

'No, a blend.'

'Which one?'

'The cheapest one you have.' I wanted it to burn me when I drank it.

Half an hour later I sat down at the rear of the next bus going to my hometown just as the engine roared and its huge metal body rattled and shuddered into life on the concourse. Outside there was sunshine everywhere. A landscape obliterated by light. A burning blue day filled with a terrible distance. As I unscrewed the cap from the whisky, took a long drink, then leant my head against the window, it looked as if the entire city could disappear at any moment. The light and the whisky merged with the vibrations of the bus into a river of memory that worked its way inside me and flowed through my body. I could feel it drift into my bones, loosen my spirit, and just as I feel asleep, take the pennies from my eyes.

The last time I travelled home on a bus I was with my father. I was seven years old and I'd been living with him in the north of England since my parents split-up the year before. He said I was going to stay with my mum for a couple of days while he took care of some business. Ours was the first bus to depart that morning and I was still wearing my pyjama top beneath my blue parka and was barely awake as the bus pulled out of Blackburn bus station. A washed-out dawn seeped into the day through a fissure stretched across the horizon and huge dark clouds hung above the town and the surrounding country like billowing plumes of coal dust. As we drove along narrow deserted streets lined with redbrick terraced houses, picking up speed as we progressed towards the outskirts of town, we passed through that melancholy landscape that is any UK town viewed from a bus window at six am. It felt like we were fleeing an area that was under quarantine. The further we travelled the chattier and more excitable the other passengers became, like they couldn't believe they were actually going to make it out of there. Twenty minutes later, when we swung onto the M6 at speed and started heading north, everyone seemed to breathe a collective sigh of relief and settle down into the journey. My father read a book and I looked out the window determined to count all the lampposts we passed on our way to Scotland. I kept trying but I never made it beyond fifty. My gaze would shift to road kill on the hard shoulder or a bird of prey hovering above a field or a lamppost would be erased by a shaft of light breaking through the clouds and I'd lose count and need to start all over again.

After a few hours most of the other passengers started rummaging around in their bags unpacking the food they'd brought. I hadn't eaten since the day before and the warm floral clouds of tea and soup steaming from flasks and the noise of bags of crisps being torn open and sandwiches being unwrapped made my stomach ache. We didn't have any food, other than the clothes we were wearing and the paperback my father was carrying, we didn't have anything else with us at all.

'Do you want something to eat?' My father asked as I strained and fidgeted in my seat with hunger.

'Yeah, I'm starving,' I told him.

'We're due to stop soon, I'll get you something then. What would you like?'

'Pizza.'

'*Pizza?*'

'Yeah.'

'What sort of pizza?'

'Ham and pineapple.'

'Hawaiian pizza, for breakfast?'

'Uh-huh,' I beamed.

'Hawaiian pizza it is then,' he smiled.

Ten minutes later we drifted up off a slip road and began to make our way through the centre of a town. The driver announced over the tannoy that we'd be stopping for a thirty-minute break and that the passengers were free to come and go as they pleased, provided they were back on the bus in time to leave. My father said he'd spotted someplace he could get food and that I was to stay in my seat and not to move before he got back, no matter what. It was an old bus station and dingy and cheerless inside. A few strip-lights snapped and flickered beneath the roof and a cold breeze tinged with petrol and oil drifted in through the open door of the bus. I sat in the half-light of the interior watching the red digits of the LCD clock above the driver's seat tumble into numbers while the other passengers got off. The numbers glowed the same soft red as the little votive candles that burned in the church we used to attend and sitting there I experienced a sadness like the one I felt while sitting on after the end of mass on Sunday evenings when everyone else had left.

Some of the passengers went into the terminal to buy a magazine at the news-stand or to use the toilet. Others stood by the side of the bus stretching their legs or smoking. After twenty minutes most of the passengers were back onboard packing away their things. After thirty a few stragglers hurried on, smiling and apologising as they passed the driver. Then there was only one guy still out there, standing next to the door of the bus smoking a cigarette, frantically sucking on it like he was trying to deflate all his troubles. The driver told him to get a move on and he took a long last drag and then he was on the bus and in his seat too. There was no sign of my father.

After several minutes of continually checking his watch, then the little chrome tally counter he was holding, like he was willing another digit to appear in the display, the driver edged the bus forward until its bumper protruded just beyond the entrance to the station. He kept straining his body over the steering wheel, trying to look up and down the street as far as he could. It was raining a little, and like a human metronome, between each sweep of the windscreen wipers he'd look left, then right, then when the rain covered the window again, he'd glance back at me. I could see he was becoming increasingly agitated and after a few minutes he slapped the steering wheel with both hands then cut the engine and got off the bus and walked out of the station. He stood on the pavement looking up and down the road while all around me the passengers voiced their unhappiness at not having departed. When the drizzle suddenly became a deluge, the driver ran back onto the bus and sat down and hit the ignition. Everyone knew the cause of the delay and someone near the back shouted that I should get off and wait for my father at lost property. Someone else suggested calling the police. Speaking over the tannoy, the driver told the passengers that he wasn't allowed to let me off on my own, but that he'd only wait two more minutes then he'd leave. I was a seven-year-old boy who'd grown up hard and never called my father *dad* or *daddy* or any of that shit, and now I was crying like a baby and wanted my mum and for the three of us to be together, instead of being on this bus on my own with no idea what was going to happen to me. I felt dizzy and sick – as if I'd suddenly realised the reason I couldn't tell the earth was spinning so quickly was because I was spinning with it. It felt like everything around me was losing its mooring and I wanted to drop to my knees and hold on to the world. The tears were streaming down my face and I was whispering, imploring God to bring my father back. And then we began to pull out of the bus station and I tore myself from my seat and ran to the driver, begging him not to leave. I was terrified and crying uncontrollably, but he wouldn't stop to wait for my father or to let me off. He said there was nothing he could do about it, that he had to stick to the schedule. Then we turned onto the road and the driver was swearing at me, saying it was my father's own fucking fault and that the authorities would deal with both of us later. We were out on the street now and he was shifting down through the gears and the bus was picking up speed. Through a fog of tears and sighs and with my chest heaving, I kept repeating, '*But we can't leave my daddy, please, my daddy, my daddy.*' Then there was a banging on the door and my father was running alongside the bus in the torrential rain, thumping the door with the palm of his hand. I was sure he was going to slip and stumble under the wheels and I was screaming for the driver to stop and finally he did.

My father clambered up the steps cursing the driver and anyone else who even glanced at him as he walked back to his seat. When he sat down he was breathless and his clothes were soaked and sticking heavily to his skin. I felt awful for him and wanted to scream at the passengers to stop commenting and tutting and looking at us.

'I did order your pizza, it just took them too bloody long to cook it,' he said without turning to look at me, 'I promise I'll get you whatever you want when we get off the bus back home.'

I knew he was lying about the pizza because I could smell the whisky on his breath. I didn't care though, I was just glad he was beside me. 'I'm not even hungry and I hate pizza anyway,' I told him. He didn't answer me, he was somewhere else now, deep inside his shame and anger. Looking at him, I wanted to start crying all over again, but I didn't. I swallowed the sorrow fluttering in my chest and narrowed my eyes as much as I could to keep my tears in check, because I knew that if I started crying, his shame would disappear and there would only be anger.

After ten minutes he fell asleep and I stared at the beads of rainwater streaking across the window, imagining they were tiny mercurial comets that chimed like little glass bells and disappeared when they collided with one another. For mile after mile I listened to them toll, losing myself in them and dying over and over again. Outside the world didn't know or care about what had happened. We drove on and life passed by like scenes from a movie I would never play a part in. I had the feeling I was driving away from what was left of my childhood and that there was no way back.

That evening when we approached my mum's house my father told me he'd wait around the corner so that I could surprise her when she came to the door. I rang the bell and kept ringing, but no one answered. After five minutes I went to find my father and he'd gone. I walked back to my mum's and sat on the front step waiting for either of them to return. My mum showed up hours later, it was dark, and she was drunk and with a guy I'd never seen before. I still hadn't eaten, so she made me toast with sugar sprinkled on it and milky tea, which I drank on my own in the kitchen while she sat with the guy in the living room. Afterwards she told me to get to bed and said we'd talk in the morning. I didn't need to change as I still had my pyjama top on. I just took off my jacket and trousers and curled up into a ball in the bed in the spare room.

As I lay there in the dark I felt like the loneliest person in the world and realized for the first time how tiny and insignificant I was. How one day I would die and so would everyone I knew and there was nothing I could do about it. I was alone, and I understood that from now on this was how it would always be. Regardless of where I was or who I was with, I would never feel like I was home. I would always be moving away.

When I got up the next day the guy from the night before had gone. There were others, but I never saw him again. It turned out my father hadn't phoned ahead to say I was coming or bothered to check beforehand to see if my mum would be home. She was surprised to see me, but not in the way I'd expected. I knew my father wasn't coming back for me, that I wasn't going to see him for a long time. I didn't imagine it would be forever.

I awoke with someone gently shaking my arm and looked up to see the bus driver standing beside me.

'Are you alright?' He asked.

'Yeah, I think so,' I told him.

'It looks like you got through a fair bit of that,' he said pointing to the bottle of whisky on the seat beside me.

To the side of the driver, framed by the window, the evening sky looked like a picture-postcard. It was cool and calm and there were no clouds, only the crisscrossing contrails of jetliners breaking up and drifting across the sky in a series of fiery rags. It looked like the evening was letting go of everything.

'Where am I?' I asked.

'You missed all the stops and went right round mate, you're back in Glasgow.'

The words scratched into the lamppost, the beckoning cat, the message on the off-licence window, things like that were always happening to me. I mean, every time I had a good intention or was determined to see something through to its conclusion, something unexpected would intervene and derail me. For a while I told myself it was coincidence, but it happened so often I began to wonder if maybe it wasn't coincidence, but providence. Then again, I suppose if you try hard enough or don't bother trying at all, you'll always see what you want to see and miss what you want to miss. The truth is, there are countless signs like the ones I saw in towns and cities all over the world. Obscure symbols, words written by people in random places, and they probably don't tell or reveal anything to us at all, besides the fact that we're all lost.

RANJIT SAIMBI

Near Llandaff

I'm near Llandaff bro, I'll see you there. I was actually in Fairwater so it wouldn't take too long to get there, but it's better to lock those boys in. They said they'd be driving.

Black Audi A1 just down by the cathedral man. We'll see you there.

It was a minging day to be walking I tell you. Proper overcast, threatening to rain any minute. I pull my hoodie up around my head. I'm wearing all black, full Nike tracksuit, and I'm striding at speed as the cars go by. I look like any youth, but I'm illicit. Fingering the little bag of weed in the front pocket of my hoodie. Yea it's good shit man, is what I usually say, even if I'm selling Sainsbury's thyme to kids in school. But this stuff is banging, proper gets you block up man.

I got it from this Somali boy from London the other week, he pulled up in a BMW out in Penarth. Quiet there like. No one going to see anything, but I was nervous to be fair. Somalis bro. They freak me out, always talking in that language – Arabic or something. But there were four of them, and even when I handed over the cash I was nervous like. I can handle myself, but they have those faces where you never know where you stand. Yea boss you got tha monee, all smiling, but there's definitely something going on there like.

Still Dre and the bass is detonating through me. What can I say? Cal-i-for-ni-A. Nah Big Ego's, that's the one, and my face is like a gargoyle set in stone. You know not to fuck with me as I stride past. I set my shoulder rigid, hang it out there as a guy walks past and catch him with a spiteful edge. With a stumble he turns back to look at me and sees a look like thunder. Where niggas die everyday over some shit they say. Prick I say over my breath so he hears.

I'm a bit high like, smoked some of that draw before I left. Always smoking that shit my missus shouted as I swung the door behind me: sitting on the sofa with the sprog, Hobnob crumbs on creaking leather, Kardashians on the telly. Fuckin' chill out luv. Gotta test out the product don't I.

Eminem now. I see this kid's bike, like a beached fish on a front lawn, and without breaking stride and with a look over my shoulder, I grab it and cycle off. I can hear family noise wafting out through the open front door so I cycle quickly. There's vomit on his sweater already, mom's spaghetti. I'm whooping in my head as the wind blows across my face, and my eyes water. Haha yes bro, literally just nicked this bike on my way, I'll say when I see those boys.

We actually all went to the same school together. A cathedral school, not far from the cathedral where I'm meant to be meeting them. It was pretty posh I must admit.

And I was proper naughty.

I got suspended once for fighting, but it was this kid that everyone in the year used to bully. The kid was the biggest nerd, always with his hand in the air before Miss even finished her sentence. I battered him to be fair, but he had been needling me and deserved it bro. He called me thick, bottom set maths. But it was the way he looked at me too, like he really meant it.

So I absolutely laid him out. And the deputy-head was the one who disciplined me. I felt bad then, said that he appreciated things weren't well at home, but I had given him no choice. My shirt was untucked with a fat stubby tie, and it was the summer term. I remember the damp smell of mud and grass because I'd been told to go straight from the playground to the deputy's office.

You have to go right past the school playing fields to get to the cathedral. It looks the same as I free-wheel past. Even though it's cold as fuck, and my hands are like Tesco fish fingers on these handlebars, there are some lads out playing cricket. I haven't played in years bro. Literally I was so sick. I've got one hand fingering the baggie still as I cycle past. In assembly you'd get given a cricket ball if you scored a half ton and I got given so many of them, smiling mischievously as I got up to collect the new cricket ball off the deputy-head – I'd much rather see you like this than under the usual circumstances. I got a cricket bat too for scoring a century once. Kookaburra. Mum left dad around then so I only had this shite V100. I remember that summer smashing new balls against that bat, and they left a red smudge on the wood. You'd just hear the echo of the ball on the bat, bouncing around the field like someone had dropped something.

The weed's wearing off now. So annoying man. Everything seems less somehow, and I'm nearly at the cathedral. Yes boys, how's it going, and there's two lads in a black Audi A1 parked up.There's music tumbling out the open windows even though it's cold. Let's have a fag bruv, and one of them obliges because I'm the dealer, and there's always this funny dynamic like.

Haven't see you in years bruv. In uni is it? I say this while breathing out the fag smoke, and give him back the lighter. I'm not really listening to the answer. Smoke a lot up there is it? Yea man, blazing everyday bruv. Ah wicked, bet the parties are bare good. I'm going Bristol to see this DJ next month, gonna be sick, selling bare draw to students man.

What about you bruv, and I half recognise the other one as one of these kids from school. He's smoking a straight, and ashing it every two seconds with his arm hanging out the window. I swear we was in the same class. History he says. Fucking hell yea, and he was. He was one of the other nerd kids like, but I liked him from memory. Not like that kid I laid out that time. With Mr Thomas wasn't it? Yea he said. Fuckin' ell I used to drive him mad, me and Lloyd just makin' fartin' noises at the back like. The guy laughed again. He had a smart jumper on, and when he asked if the weed was good, his voice didn't sound anywhere near as Cardiff as I thought it would.

You in London are you, bruv? I picked up off these Somali lads from London, fucking hell man, Somalis I swear. Always out to rob you innit. They both laughed at this, and the one who gave me a cigarette to make conversation and with a grin said – That can't be your real bike bro.

This was my moment! Haha yes bro, literally just nicked this bike on my way I say drawing on the cigarette, and to be fair the bike is clearly not mine. It's pink and tiny, laying on the ground next to the wheel of the Audi. Both lads laugh incredulously now. You're so funny man, the one I half remember from school says, but I wonder if he's taking the piss because he glances at the one who gave me a fag. Sorry little girl, need to sell some drugs like! And we're all laughing again.

I roll a joint and spark it. No offence to these lads but they stayed at posh school so I think I'm qualified to roll a better zoot than they are. I have all the paraphernalia I need: lush metal grinder from the Dam, roach card and some big silvers. I roll an absolute cone, and we're chilling there smoking it, down past the cathedral. We left the car parked up, and we're chilling behind some trees by the path. A dog walker sees us, but who gives a fuck. It's good weed, and the smoke sits flat on the air around us. My eyes feel full, and I'm bang up for talking.

Bro do you remember how sick you were at cricket man, says the one who gave me the fag. Ha yes bro I used to absolutely smash it round the park. Genuinely my average was infinity one season no joke and we're all laughing loads now, and their faces look all tinged with grey like the weed smoke is in their skin. Do you play much now, or? Nah man. I went college didn't I and their facilities were shit bro I swear. Didn't bother with county either during sixth form man, so much training and then I got into the sticky-icky! They laugh again and I change the topic.

What about you man, I say to the one I half remember, cos I know the other guy a bit better. Oh wow, law school is it? Might need your help one day man, if I keep going with the game bro. I'm joking when I say this, but my mate got sent down last year. He was selling coke though, and you know how it is if you get into that shit man. He got pulled over on the M4 by an undercover car, proper shit, because he was picking up a load from these Albanian guys. Serious stuff man. The lad laughs, but then he starts explaining about how criminal law doesn't pay and about how he wants to do company law or some shit. I'm not fully following to be honest. Different world bruv.

Good green, innit? I say changing topic again. Yea man, not too harsh at all, and then we go silent for a bit, and you can hear the wind rustle the leaves, and maybe a lonely bird in the distance.

The spliff's done and I flick it away into some bushes. Well lads, next time you're down from uni give me a buzz like, or if you want a load before you go back let me know. I can put a call in to my guy if it's a few ounces. We walk back to the black Audi, and it's getting darker and more cold. They get in, the beams shoot mesmerising light, and the wheels make this satisfying gravelly noise as the car pulls away. Nice one man, says the one I know better out the window, but the other one has his head in his phone. I don't feel like riding this stupid pink bike now, so I wheel it alongside me, and I don't feel like going past the cathedral school either, so I carry on along the path into the woods behind the cathedral.

I think I can get home that way.

I'm not striding this time as I walk. I don't feel like listening to my music either, so the ear buds dangle out the top my hoodie, swinging with each step. I've pulled my sleeves over my hands, and every now and again I cup them and breathe warm breath on them. It's freezing.

The path splits into two ahead of me, and I take the one which has less wear. I think it heads to the river because I can hear the low rumble of rushing water, but I can't be sure. I wonder for a second where the other one leads, but the river is loud now, the Taff I think. It's fully dark so all I see are the choppy shadows of waves roaring past. Behind me the cathedral stands in the distance like a silent sentinel. Fuck this stupid pink bike bro I think, and pivoting like a hammer thrower, I hurl the stupid pink bike into the river.

It takes silent flight against the dark grey sky, before the rushing torrent takes it. There's not even a splashing noise because the river roars so loudly. That was like one of my cricket hook shots it was. Where you generate all this power from your body's rotation. I'm blowing after that and my breath forms little clouds in the air around me like cigarette smoke.

I keep walking along the path – apart from the river all I can hear is the crunch of my trainers on the gravel. It's just me now so I follow the path along the river, wherever it takes me.

Likes

When I got out of the shower, it wasn't a surprise that Michael had had left for work. Sometimes, if I was lucky, he'd hurriedly kiss me goodbye in a mimic of intimacy. The banana, which he'd unloaded from his backpack last night, remained on my dressing table. Michael had written my name into the curve of the skin with a black marker pen. It was blooming spots of brown.

Open Instagram.
Take photo.
Select Filter.
Witty tagline: *Fruity.*
Three emojis.
Seven hashtags.
Post.

One like. Two likes. Three likes, four.
Five likes, six likes, seven likes, more.

'See you later, Amy,' Annie called from the top of the stairs. 'Was that Michael I heard sneaking out this morning?'

Annie's man never came in late at night and snuck out with the sun. He would eat dinner with her and ask me if I'd had a nice day at work as I waited for my pasta to soften. They took smiling selfies at National Trust properties on Sunday afternoons, their commonplace happiness taunting virtual onlookers. Or just me.

'Oh God, *sorry.* I told him to be quiet. Did he wake you?'

The first time Michael had stayed over, we fell in at 3 am. In my bedroom he was slowly, painfully slowly, pushing his hands up my legs when we were interrupted by WhatsApps from Annie asking us to keep it down.

'Did you have a nice evening?'

Did I have a nice evening? Michael had come round at 11 pm, pulled off my tights and went down on me for twenty minutes. Then we enjoyed a bit of light choking before he fucked me from behind. I wouldn't tell

Annie that. I like to think that she and her boyfriend only ever have sex on ceremonial occasions like the final of Wimbledon or the Queen's Birthday.

'Yes, I suppose.'

On the Northern Line, a man's damp armpit hovered above my ear. I could feel my foundation slipping down my neck and onto my newly laundered silk blouse. I envisaged myself arriving into Old Street rotting with perspiration, my fingernails lined with grime.

As the tube shuddered into Camden Town, the man wiped his brow with a filthy hand. More people pushed into the cramped carriage and I closed my eyes. When I got into the office, I was going to drink a fresh mint tea and answer my emails in a precise and utilitarian fashion. I could almost hear the comforting clack of my clean fingers on my smooth Apple keyboard. Then, and only then, I would look at how many likes I had on Instagram, scroll through Twitter and reply to my WhatsApps.

Midday. I did it. I managed it. Blouse still intact. I flicked my iPhone off airplane mode and reapplied my makeup in the work bathroom. When I looked down I would see emails, emojis and likes, likes, likes. I loved listening to the repeated vibrate of my phone on the counter.

@david_thornton_89 liked your photo.

'Is that you, Amy?' Annie called down the hall as I shut the front door. I could hear her clattering about in the kitchen.

'Yes!' I called. 'Just going to have a shower. I'm all sweaty from the tube.'

I locked myself in the bathroom, turned the shower on and sat down on edge of the bath. I hadn't turned my phone on since lunchtime. Each time I had looked at the dark screen I imagined David's breath on my neck, his cock pushing at my wet knickers and my hands gripping the cum-stained cover of his duvet. But, what if he'd messaged me? What if he missed me? What if he wanted, no needed, me back? I turned it on.

My iPhone caught onto our Wi-Fi and sprang into life with emails, WhatsApps, retweets, DMs, life, love, likes. I stared at the screen and forced my thumb to touch him: *@david_thornton_89*.

An exotic location, tightly cropped with a white border. A pretty girl in black and white grinning against a graffitied wall. A well-lit avocado and poached egg brunch. A David Foster Wallace novel against a geometric background. The same girl in Paris outside the Pompidou Centre. The retreating back of the same girl with a washed-out Sussex backdrop. The same girl again in Clarendon, the same girl again in Mayfair, the same girl again in Juno, again, again, again.

What had I done since we'd last seen each other a year ago? Watched Netflix. Gone on a couple of unglamorous holidays. Shagged three, no two, men. Whereas David had seventy-four likes, ninety-two likes, one hundred and seventeen likes. I stopped counting.

'Amy?' Annie asked outside the door. 'I'm making risotto, do you want some?'

'Sure.'

'Well, hurry up then. *University Challenge* is almost on.'

Open Instagram.
Take photo.
Select Filter.
Witty tagline: *Amazing @AnnabelleP has made us a gluttonous feast for Monday night with Paxman*
Three emojis.
Seven hashtags.
Post.

One like. Two likes. Three likes, four.
Five likes, six likes, seven likes, more.

'Hey, it's me. It's Amy. Where are you?'

'Out with some of the work lot,' Michael said. He had to raise his voice. 'Were we supposed to do something tonight?'

'No... I just thought you mentioned you weren't doing anything,' I said. I had the phone caught between my shoulder and ear and I opened another window on my browser. 'Annie is out, so you could come over.'

My fingers danced over the keys: *@david_thornton_89.*

'I think I'm going to stay here a bit... I've had a hard week.'

David's profile picture was of him with his arm wrapped snugly around the girl from Instagram. They were both grinning at the camera.

'Have you eaten yet?' I asked, staring at David. His Twitter biography confirmed previously held knowledge: Software Engineer, South London.

'I'll just grab something at the pub or get a burger on the way home.'

I scrolled through his pithy comments on tech news, occasional comments about Spurs and endless flirting, bantering, online fucking with *@IsobelHunter.*

'Michael?' I asked as the chattering noise in the pub rose. 'Are we still going to do something tomorrow?'

@IsobelHunter's profile was private. Her banner image was an old photo of Beyoncé and Jay Z. In her profile picture, her hair was pulled over her face. Her About Me told me that she worked for an art gallery in Mayfair and lived in Peckham.

'Let's just play it by ear.'

She had 800 Twitter followers, but her profile was private. What kind of fucking game was she playing? Maybe she had a niche fashion blog. Or maybe she had made her profile private because she was being trolled after a viral blog post she'd written on intersectional feminism. Maybe she had a book deal. Maybe writers from *Buzzfeed* replied to her effortlessly great Tweets. Maybe she had a podcast with all her super amazing friends which was recommended by *The Guardian*. Fuck, how many Instagram followers did she have?

'Yeah, sure.'

Private, again. Would she know who I was if I requested to follow her? Maybe she and David had long conversations about me. Maybe they laughed about how much he didn't love me. Maybe he told her that he'd never known real, deep, proper love until he'd met her.

'I've got to go, Amy. My battery is running out.'

Maybe I was mentioned in their hour-long conversations about love with a pitying look and a sad smile. I'm so lucky to have found you, David would say. I could never take Amy seriously. I didn't like her enough, she didn't smell like you, love like you, didn't get wet like you, kiss like you, fuck like you, she wasn't like you, it wasn't like this.

'Sure. Just let me know about tomorrow.'

Maybe they looked at my Twitter and Instagram and laughed. Look at her pitiful amount of followers, her laughable excuse for a career and the greys threading through her hair. How bone-shatteringly sad, she would say. How heart-stoppingly pathetic, he would say. What has she done? What will she ever do? Her name isn't made for great things, she'll fade away, sink without a trace, lost forever, another sad girl online desperately refreshing her OkCupid profile, swiping through Tinder until the end of the world.

'Sure. Bye, Amy.'

I hung up, cursed *@IsobelHunter* into Google and felt bile swell up my throat when different versions of her smiling face appeared on my screen.

Michael WhatsApped me on Saturday evening asking if I wanted to come round. I didn't reply for four hours and, when I did, I suggested the pub on Sunday afternoon. I didn't want him to think that I had spent most of Saturday endlessly scrolling through *@IsobelHunter*'s best friend's wedding pictures while I waited for him to message me. I wanted him to think I was doing something important, like reading a David Foster Wallace novel at some bar in Peckham with my best friend who had just got married. Or whatever people do on a Saturday.

David had guest-starred in *@IsobelHunter's* best friend's wedding. His eyes looked through the camera and straight into my sexless bedroom. Look at you, he smirked from my screen, watching me on a Saturday afternoon when you could be out doing something more worthwhile with your time. You're sad, you're pathetic, you're jealous of me. You'll never get over me, you'll never move past this, you'll never find what I've found. You're shallow, screen-addicted and sad. You'll think of me when you die and I don't even remember your name.

'Hey,' Michael said. He was twenty minutes late. His eyes were rimmed with red, his shoulders stooped and his hands were shoved in his pockets. 'Shall we go in? I'm desperate for a pint.'

The pub I'd suggested was quite nice. It was full of clear-skinned couples huddled over board games with bottles of wine. I wanted to be one of those women. I bet they all had clean flats filled with houseplants. I bet they never had to deal with hungover, lazy, non-monogamous guys who they regretted speaking to at a house party. I bet their lives involved pay-rises, yoga and self-actualization.

I chose one of the artfully-aged wood tables next to a steamed-up window. I drew a heart on it. I decided not to take a photo of it because my face might be reflected back.

'I'm so hungover,' Michael said. He put his forehead on the table to demonstrate his self-inflicted suffering. 'I didn't get home until, like, 4 am.'

I knew how this was supposed to go: he expected pity and a blow job.

'Yeah. I saw on your Instagram.'

The image in question had shit composition and had so far received three likes. If it were mine, I'd have deleted it after a couple of hours. I once read that women were far better at social media than men. We are made to be liked, made to forgo punctuation for laughs and accumulate favourites. Made to write pithy observations on the bus home and have them repeated back to us by unimaginative men at house parties. To be patronised as girls, silly and vain for wanting to control the gaze with filters and angles.

'Pint? Actually, can we sit outside so I can have a cigarette?'

'It's freezing outside. Nobody will be out there.'

'They'll have heaters. Come on, Amy. I'm so hungover. It'll make me feel better.'

'Fine.' I stood back up, scraping the chair with me. I hope it made him wince, I hope it made him want to vomit up his night out, I hope it made him regret shagging all those other women and treating me a disposable girl who he could fuck late at night. 'I'll grab Scrabble.'

'Scrabble, really?' He pushed himself back onto his feet and rolled his eyes. 'My mind is too fried for that.'

'Mine isn't.'

I was wrong. People were outside; a couple sat under a heater. They had a bottle of half-finished red wine and were wrapped up in knitted scarves and hats. A Guess Who? was set out in front of them, but they'd abandoned all competition and were holding up cards, laughing at the cardboard portraits. Their iPhones were laid next to each other on the side of the table, screens down and silent.

'I'd rather play Guess Who?,' Michael grumbled as I opened the box. The pearl tiles were worn out and someone had attacked the board with a crayon. 'You set up and I'll get the drinks.'

When he was back inside, I watched the woman at the other table. She grabbed her phone and took a photo of the man holding up a card from the Guess Who? set.

'One more, one more. I'm going to send it to Katy. Stop laughing, it looks just like you!'

'This lad's beard is ginger. Mine is darker.'

'Yours is ginger.'

She looked up from her phone as she said it. A private joke, a life shared, worlds aligned. He posed again with the card, laughing as she took the photo. The flash from her iPhone lit up his grinning face, neither of them caring about the red wine stains on his teeth or the bad angle.

Open Instagram.
Take photo.
Select Filter.
Witty tagline: *A dream Sunday playing Scrabble and drinking beer with @michaelhopkin.*
Three emojis.
Seven hashtags.
Post.

One like. Two likes. Three likes, four.
Five likes, six likes, seven likes, more.

TIM CRAIG

The Grand Finale

Even by his own high standards, The Great Fantoni's world tour had been a triumph. The crowds had turned out in their thousands to welcome him wherever he went and the newspaper reviews had proclaimed the show his best yet.

When the magician finally arrived home, he handed his coat and jacket to his wife and announced that he would be going straight to bed.

Mrs Great Fantoni wished her husband a good night and, although she was tired herself, said that she would unpack his things for him before retiring.

After he had gone up, she dragged his large, monogrammed trunk down the hallway and into the sitting room. There, she undid the gold clasps, lifted the heavy lid, and took out a hinged leather portmanteau.

From this, she removed a vintage suitcase, which she noted still bore the faded destination label from their honeymoon. Inside the suitcase was a hand-tooled crocodile-skin valise, which, in turn, held an old canvas rucksack.

Scrunched up in the rucksack was a blue sports holdall, from which she pulled a plastic supermarket bag containing her husband's cheap floral wash bag.

She unzipped the wash bag and took out his orange plastic toothbrush holder. She popped this open to discover an empty foil condom packet from which, with a flourish – and the sound of triumphant applause ringing in her ears – she extracted the children, the house and half the money.

JIM GLEESON

Nan

Granny Coulter sat with prayer beads round her knuckles, her cup cold between her fingers, killing time. The boss men wanted her grandson outside in twenty minutes. He was hunched on the couch in her little front room, racing cars on a laptop, hadn't said much since she'd taken in his favourite meal. If that boy had stuck to playing games, she might not be waiting to walk him out when the van arrived, might not have had the call. 'That boy took the wrong car this time. We know your stock, we'll go easy once, it'll only be the one knee, but that wee pup better learn. Bring him out at nine. If we have to come looking we'll do the pair of them.' He'd learn all right, every twisted step would be a lesson. Outside, small boys played football, swinging their legs and squealing with the joy of it. She remembered the feathery weight and the smell of him, that beautiful boy, and thinking of the savage hurt to come almost broke her in two, but she stayed silent. She wouldn't weep, wish that life was different, knock on the church door for a quiet word or call the police, wouldn't waste her time. A van rumbled up outside, revving, with too much business and too many other boys to linger long. 'It's time,' she said, 'but I'll be here.' 'Nan', he said, then he was gone. She closed the door and waited for the hospital call.

MOLIA DUMBLETON

What Real Men Wish They Dreamed

On the day his buddy blew his hand off on a sack of premature ANFO, The Miner wrapped the frizzled hand in his favorite flannel shirt and set it next to him on the bench-seat of his truck while his buddy sat passenger, bleeding more than he'd ever seen someone bleed and howling like he'd only ever heard from dogs. The nurses didn't bring the hand back after he handed it to them in the ER, which meant The Miner hadn't seen his shirt again neither, and he was rattling with cold by the time they drugged his buddy into dumb silence and told The Miner to go home and wash up, rest. At home he sat on the couch and shook so hard his dog wouldn't even sit with him.

When The Miner finally felt sleep coming from far off, he leaned over onto the scratchy cushions and tried to hook it, gentle but steady, and tug it to him like a fish on a line. He made a wish for what he would like to dream: Not of coal or blood, or gold, or even his now-gone shirt, which he had liked to ball up under his head for sleeping, and which he missed now. But of his dead mother, who whenever he had gotten a hole, used to darn it right on his foot while he was still wearing it. Tickling his toes with her rounded needle-eye and winking at him, tease-scolding *Don't you dare wiggle, now.*

RUTH BRANDT

Lucky Underpants

We stand up and kiss and then we sit down and kiss and before long we're lying on the half circle rug. She is above me and her tongue slips into my mouth and I am ever so grateful. This is going to be fantastic, me and Rebecca on the rug. God, this is the best.

Then I hear her toe tapping on the floorboard. For a moment I try to ignore the regular tap-tapping before I realise that the rhythm syncopates with the movement of her mouth and I cannot help but think of gnawing. And then I am thinking animals, a moose chewing cud in particular. And then I'm wondering why I'm thinking of a moose, and anyway, does a moose even chew cud? And just as I'm about to pull my head away from the pressure of her lips she twists off me and sits statue still. I can't help checking her feet, the boot sole that must have been responsible for the tapping.

'Don't you want to?' she says.

I sit up and rest my chin on her shoulder, a bit like one calf on another, and can't think of anything other than, 'How many stomachs does a cow have?'

'Fucking Attenborough,' she says and I am no further forward with knowing whether my lucky underpants have been successful or not.

'I think it's five,' I say.

'Nothing happened,' she says. 'Remember that. Nothing happened.'

ELIZABETH EDELGLASS

Partial

My grandmother had a partial bridge, kept in a glass by her bed while she slept, so my mother said. To me, Grandma's smile looked perfect, when she let me win at Gin Rummy. Her lips, when she pursed them to kiss my cheek, marred only by laugh lines. A partial bridge can crack, *did* crack, my mother said. Easily replaced, she said, all you need is money.

My mother had a partial knee, five years ago, with a ten-year warranty. Now she can kneel to vroom cars on the floor with her great-grandson, who chortles, milk teeth perfect as pearls. *My* grandson, that boy Mom can dandle on said knee, playing pat-a-cake, licking pretend frosting off sweet baby fingers. Five more years of pat-a-cake, six if she's lucky, 'til she'll need to replace that knee once again. Easy as buying a new car, or a vacuum cleaner, she says. Except for the pain, and the fear, unmentioned.

My son, who fathered that delectable baby, is in partial remission. *Remission*, the doctor says on the last day of treatment, *partial*. We're alone in the room, the three of us, doctor, son, and me. Son's wife at home on pat-a-cake duty. The doctor is bald, like my nodding son. The son I always smiled for through shots and stitches, earaches and broken bones. That smile meant to say all will be okay. I smile for him now, with all my teeth. It's my heart in a glass, only partially broken.

EMMA NEALE

Courtship

He wooed me many ways: tried everything from lending books to night-dancing, blood starry with lager.

We talked, yet it wasn't working. So he left the country, asking if he could keep in touch.

His letters – handwritten – soon arrived. He laughs when I say this, but it was seduction by punctuation. As if each semi-colon was someone leaning forward, head bubbling with the future; or perhaps an athlete, leaping for the catch. Such elegance and rhythm.

Bud and stalk; sun and moon; hook and sinker. A bottle that's popped its cork. Or even egg and ecstatic sperm, pre-fusion.

Biographies

Daljit Nagra is from a Sikh background and was born and grew up in West London then Sheffield. He has published four books of poetry, all with Faber & Faber.

His poem 'Look We Have Coming to Dover!' won the Forward Prize for Best Individual Poem in 2004. His first collection, of the same name won the Forward Prize for Best First Collection in 2007 and the South Bank Show Decibel Award in 2008. His subsequent two collections, *Tippoo Sultan's Incredible White-Man Eating Tiger-Toy Machine!!!* and his version of the *Ramayana* were nominated for the TS Eliot Prize. In 2014 he was selected as a New Generation Poet by the PBS. In 2015 he won a Royal Society Travelling Scholarship. His latest collection is *British Museum,* which was published in 2017.

He was the inaugural Poet in Residence for Radio 4/4 Extra and teaches at Brunel University London.

Monica Ali is an award-winning, bestselling writer whose novels include *Brick Lane, In the Kitchen* and *Untold Story.* She was chosen as one of Granta's 2003 Best of Young British Novelists. Her work has been translated into 26 languages, and she has judged a number of literary prizes including as Chair of the Asian Man Booker.

Her writing has appeared in numerous publications including the *Guardian,* the *Times, The New Yorker,* and the *New York Times,* for which she is a literary reviewer. Monica has been a guest editor of BBC Radio 4's *Today* programme, and has presented several editions of the Radio 4 show, *A Point of View.* She is a Fellow of the RSA and of the Orwell Prize.

She has taught creative writing at Columbia University, New York, where she was a visiting Professor, and she is currently Distinguished Writer in Residence at the University of Surrey.

Karen Ashe was brought up in Airdrie and now lives in Glasgow with her family. 'Rebound', the first short story she ever wrote, took second place in the South China Morning Post short story competition, and she went on to complete the MLitt in Creative Writing at Glasgow University. As well as short stories, she also writes poetry, recently placing third in the FWS Easter poetry competition, and making the shortlist for the Glasgow Women's Library Short Story competition. She also writes flash fiction and has been published online in Paragraph Planet. Karen is one of Scottish Book Trust New Writer's Awardees for 2016. She has been shortlisted for the Fish Short Story and Flash Fiction prizes, and was Highly Commended in the Poetry prize in 2018. A non-fiction piece, 'Never on a Friday' was published in the Mslexia Curious Incidents section, and more recently, 'The Bearded Lady', in their Monster-themed New Writing showcase. She was Highly Commended in the Bridport Prize 2016 for her story 'The Disappeared Girl' and again in 2017 for the short story 'Girvan Blues'. Her poem 'Iceberg' was shortlisted for the Bridport prize in 2017, and the short story 'White Brick' was published in *Gutter Magazine* in 2018.

Ruth Brandt's short stories and flash fiction have appeared in anthologies and magazines, including the *Aesthetica Creative Writing Annual*, *Bristol Short Story Prize*, *Neon*, *Litro* and *The London Reader*. She has had a play performed at Theatre 503 and her poetry published in the *Irish Literary Review* and *Bunbury Magazine*. She won the Kingston University MFA Creative Writing Prize 2017 and has been nominated for the Pushcart Prize and Write Well Award. She is Writer in Residence at the Surrey Wildlife Trust.

Aifric Campbell is from Dublin and lives in the UK. Her third novel, *On the Floor*, was longlisted for the International Orange Prize 2012. Previous novels are *The Loss Adjustor* and *The Semantics of Murder*. She spent thirteen years as an investment banker at Morgan Stanley where she became the first woman managing director on the London trading floor. Her writing has appeared in *the Irish Times*, *The Guardian*, *Wall Street Journal*, *The Sunday Telegraph*, and others. Aifric holds a PhD in Critical & Creative Writing from the University of East Anglia and teaches at Imperial College, London.

Patricia Cantwell lives in Clonmel, County Tipperary, Ireland. She is a relative newcomer to the writing scene. She taught Drama for many years as well as producing and presenting a daily programme on local radio. She completed a law degree and set up her own legal practice which she ran successfully for well over twenty years. She sold her practice to concentrate on her writing. She won the 'Emerging Poet' award at the Carrick-on-Suir Writers Weekend in 2016. Two of her poems have previously been shortlisted for the Bridport Prize. She has written a novel and is seeking a publisher.

Emily Chen is a freshman pursuing studies of political economy and English at Williams College. She is the editor of *Sine Theta Magazine*, an international print-based creative arts magazine made by and for the Sino diaspora. Emily is the recipient of multiple writing recognitions, including several Gold and Silver Keys from the National Scholastic Art and Writing Awards. She was selected as a 2018 mentee of *The Adroit Journal*'s annual fiction mentorship program and a participant in two *Winter Tangerine* online workshops. In her free time, Emily enjoys reading, swimming, and avoiding all things avocado.

Catherine Chidgey lives in Ngaruawahia, New Zealand. Her honours include the Commonwealth Writers' Prize for Best First Book (Asia-Pacific), a Betty Trask Award and the Katherine Mansfield Short Story Award. Her fourth novel, *The Wish Child*, set in Nazi Germany, won the $50,000 fiction prize at the 2017 New Zealand book awards – the country's richest writing prize. Radio New Zealand called it 'a brilliant, brilliant novel...a masterpiece', and *The Times* (UK) 'a remarkable book with a stunningly original twist'. Her most recent honour is the Janet Frame Fiction Prize. Her 'found' novel, *The Beat of the Pendulum*, is released in the UK in January 2019.

Elaine Chiew is a writer based in London and Singapore. She's the editor/compiler of *Cooked Up: Food Fiction From Around the World* (New Internationalist, 2015). Her most recent stories can be found in *Unthology 10*, *Potomac Review*, *East of the Web*, and *Smokelong Quarterly*. Her fiction has won prizes (most notably the Bridport Prize 2008) and been shortlisted in competitions, including the BBC Opening Lines, Mslexia, Fish, etc, and recently named Top 50 Microfiction by *Wigleaf* and Top 25 as well as Honorable Mention in *Glimmer Train's* short story competitions. She has a law degree from Stanford University and an M.A. in Asian Art History from Goldsmiths. She researches and writes freelance on Asian art for art magazines and exhibitions, occasionally curates, and has taught short fiction at Singapore's premier School of the Arts.

Tim Craig started writing flash fiction this year. In June, one of his first stories, 'Northern Lights', won third prize in the Bath Flash Fiction Award and will be published in the forthcoming BFFA anthology. A native Mancunian, Tim now lives in Hackney in East London with his wife, three children and clinically indolent dog.

Heather Derr-Smith is a poet with four books, *Each End of the World* (Main Street Rag Press, 2005), *The Bride Minaret* (University of Akron Press, 2008), *Tongue Screw* (Spark Wheel Press, 2016), and *Thrust* winner of the Lexi Rudnitsky/Editor's Choice Award (Persea Books, 2017). Her work has appeared in Fence, Crazy Horse and Missouri Review. She is managing director of Cuvaj Se, a nonprofit supporting writers in conflict zones and post-conflict zones and divides her time mostly between Iowa and Sarajevo, Bosnia.

Patrick Doddy trained at RADA and works as an actor and voice artist. He grew up in Dublin and lives in Brighton. He is currently finishing a BA in Philosophy and Creative Writing with the Open University. He was shortlisted in the poetry section of the 2016 Bridport Prize.

Molia Dumbleton's debut collection of short fiction was named one of four finalists for the 2018 Iowa Short Fiction Award. Her stories have been awarded the Seán Ó Faoláin Story Prize; Columbia Journal Winter Fiction Award; Dromineer Literary Festival Flash Fiction Prize, and others, and appeared in journals including *The Kenyon Review*, *New England Review*, *Witness*, *Hobart*, *SmokeLong Quarterly*, *Southword Journal*, and *The Stinging Fly*, in addition to the *Bath Flash Fiction Anthologies* for 2017 and 2018. Full publications list and other info can be found at www.moliadumbleton.com.

Elizabeth Edelglass has won the *Lilith* short story contest, the William Saroyan Centennial Prize, and the Lawrence Foundation Prize from *Michigan Quarterly Review*. Her fiction has recently appeared in *New Haven Review*, *Tablet*, *Lilith*, *JewishFiction.Net*, *The Sunlight Press*, *The Ilanot Review*, and three recent anthologies, including *Best Short Stories from The Saturday Evening Post Great American Fiction Contest 2017*. Her story 'Make Lemonade' was shortlisted for the 2013 Bridport Short Story Prize. She lives in Connecticut, USA, where she is currently at work on two novels as well as short fiction and poetry.

John Freeman was born in Essex, grew up in south London and lived in Yorkshire before settling in Wales. He taught for many years at Cardiff University and now lives in the Vale of Glamorgan. His most recent books are *What Possessed Me* (Worple Press), and *Strata Smith and the Anthropocene* (Knives Forks and Spoons Press), both published in 2016. Earlier collections include *A Suite for Summer* (Worple), and *White Wings: New and Selected Prose Poems* (Contraband Books). *What Possessed Me* won the Roland Mathias Poetry Award as part of the Wales Book of the Year Awards in November 2017. His poem 'My Grandfather's Hat' won third prize in the National Poetry Competition, 2012.

Jim Gleeson was born in Tipperary, Ireland in 1961, and spent time travelling the world before settling in London at the beginning of the Nineties. He has spent the years since then observing the steady flow of change in the city, from the fall of the Iron Lady to the chaos of the financial crash, from the rise of the shining Shard to the first tremors of Brexit uncertainty. Time not taken up between family, day job and tussling with two small children is spent travelling, reading occasionally at the Brixton Book Jam and scribbling short stories which surface sometimes in a wider world.

Melissa Goodbourn grew up in the foothills of the Appalachians in North Carolina and now lives by the sea in Dunbar, Scotland. She has worked as a Social Worker and Researcher, and usually finds time to write during train commutes and after her children are asleep. Her writing was encouraged and nurtured by the local Dunbar Writing Mums group. Since then she has performed her work at the Callandar Poetry Festival and Coastword Festival as part of the Flint & Pitch Revue. Her work has been published by 404 Ink and she was shortlisted for the 2018 Scottish Book Trust New Writer's Award for Fiction.

Luisa A. Igloria was the inaugural Glasgow Distinguished Writer in Residence at Washington and Lee University (2018); and the winner of the 2015 Resurgence Prize (UK), the world's first major award for ecopoetry, selected by former UK poet laureate Sir Andrew Motion, Alice Oswald, and Jo Shapcott. Former US Poet Laureate Natasha Trethewey selected her chapbook *What is Left of Wings, I Ask* as the 2018 recipient of the Center for the Book Arts Letterpress Poetry Chapbook award. Luisa is the author of the full length works *The Buddha Wonders if She is Having a Mid-Life Crisis* (Phoenicia Publishing, Montreal, 2018), *Ode to the Heart Smaller than a Pencil Eraser* (selected by Mark Doty for the

2014 May Swenson Prize, Utah State University Press), *Night Willow* (Phoenicia Publishing, Montreal, 2014), *The Saints of Streets* (University of Santo Tomas Publishing House, 2013), *Juan Luna's Revolver* (2009 Ernest Sandeen Prize, University of Notre Dame Press), and nine other books. She is also the author of the chapbooks *Haori* (Tea & Tattered Pages Press, 2017), *Check & Balance* (Moria Press/Locofo Chaps, 2017), and *Bright as Mirrors Left in the Grass* (Kudzu House Press eChapbook selection for Spring 2015). She teaches on the faculty of the MFA Creative Writing Program at Old Dominion University, which she directed from 2009-2015. www.luisaigloria.com

Ashish Xiangyi Kumar read law at the University of Cambridge, and currently lives and works in Singapore. He has been published in *Cha*, *Cordite Poetry Review*, *Oxford Poetry*, and *Quarterly West*. He won the 2018 Writers at Work Poetry Contest and took second place in the 2017 December Fortnight Poetry Prize.

V. Sanjay Kumar was born in a town called Karaikudi in the state of Tamil Nadu. He grew up in Chennai. After an MBA degree, he set up and managed businesses in Mumbai, in investment banking, banking software, and contemporary art. He is a Director at Sakshi, a contemporary art gallery based in Bombay. He became a full-time writer in 2010. He resides currently in Bangalore, returning often to the two cities that he writes about: Chennai and Mumbai.

Daniel Lambert works in education and writes in his spare time. Born in Warrington, he has lived and worked in Liverpool, Bristol and Chester. He currently lives in North Wales with his wife and son.

Vanessa Lampert is a second year student on the Poetry School London's M.A. programme. She works as an acupuncturist in Wallingford, Oxfordshire. She likes to walk especially on coastal paths, to knit and often thinks about wild swimming.

Chetna Maroo's fiction has been published in the *Bristol Short Story Prize Anthology* and *The Cincinnati Review*. She was awarded an Honorable Mention in Ninth Letter's 2018 Literary Award. Chetna was born in Kenya and grew up in Britain. She currently lives in London.

Jenni Mazaraki is a writer based in Melbourne, Australia. She is currently working on her first novel, an extract of which was shortlisted for the 2017 Deborah Cass Prize. Her writing has also been shortlisted for the Write Around the Murray short story award 2017 and longlisted for the Margaret River Press short story prize 2018. She holds a BA in Fine Art, a BA in Visual Communication and Masters Degree in Art Therapy.

Kevin McCarthy is a poet, essayist, dramatist, novelist, geologist, and animal communicator. Publications include two nonfiction books, more than 30 poems, and 60 essays. 'Enough Sky' was commended in The Poetry Society's 2014 National Competition (UK). Please see locuto.com for funny stories, film recommendations, and Colorado perspectives.

Gerry McKeague's stories have won prizes in the Michael McLaverty Short Story competition, the Bryan McMahon Listowel Writers' Award and he has been shortlisted for the Bridport and Fish prizes. Brought up in Belfast, he now lives with his family in Geelong, Australia. He is currently working on his first novel, a WW2 murder mystery.

Simon Middleton's work has previously been shortlisted for the Bridport Prize, and featured in the 2007 Bridport Prize Junior Anthology. His poetry appears in such publications as *IOTA, Envoi, Firewords Quarterly, The Cadaverine*, and Eyewear's *Best New British and Irish Poets 2017*. He lives in Bridport with his wife and two children.

Emma Neale is a New Zealander, who has lived in both the US and England. She has a PhD in literature from University College London, and works as a freelance editor for local and international publishers. Her sixth novel, *Billy Bird* (2016), was short-listed for the Acorn Prize at the Ockham New Zealand Book Awards and long-listed for the Dublin International Literary Award. She is working on another novel and has a new book of poems, *To the Occupant*, due out from Otago University Press in 2019. She is the current editor of *Landfall,* New Zealand's oldest literary and arts journal, and she is the mother of two young sons. https://emmaneale.wordpress.com/

Corrina O'Beirne was born in Dorset and now lives in Brighton. She was awarded a Creative Writing MA with Distinction from University of Chichester in 2015. Her play *Come On In, We're Open* was shortlisted in the Kenneth Branagh award for new drama writing. Her monologue *Mucky* was shortlisted in Five and Ten competition monologue competition run by Gwyn Hall Theatre. Corrina is working on her first novel and short story collection.

Ryan O'Connor spent six months travelling alone across America on Greyhound buses when he was sixteen years old, a journey that set the tone for a peripatetic life in which the only constant has been his writing. Earlier this year Ryan received the Next Chapter Award from the Scottish Book Trust. John Burnside, a judge on the panel, has subsequently gone on to support and endorse Ryan's work, saying of *The Speed of Falling*, Ryan's novel in progress, 'What is exceptional, and admirable, is that, in a field where it would be so easy to take an imitative route, *The Speed of Falling*, has a remarkable shape and depth and is an original work in its own right. I cannot wait to read the completed book, and I cannot say strongly enough how important it is to support it.' Having recently become a father, Ryan lives in the south side of Glasgow with his partner and their child.

Mark Paffard is 63. He shares poems (and pints) with good friends who include published poets. Since being able to work part-time he has also finished a novel (yet to be published) and contributed articles to the *Kipling Journal*.

Sam Phipps grew up in west London and lives in Edinburgh, where he works as a journalist and vintage bus operator. In 2016 he took an online course run by Liz Berry at the National Writing Centre. He has a stack of poems in varying states of completion that he wants to turn into a first collection.

Ranjit Saimbi is a debut writer, and Bridport entrant. His family are of the Ugandan Asian diaspora, expelled from Uganda in the 1970s, and now settled in the UK. He was born in Cardiff, where he spent his formative years and graduated from Durham University with a first-class honours in English Literature. He now lives in London where he practices as a lawyer at an international law firm. He suspects that he would better served writing, and hopes that being Highly Commended for the Bridport Prize 2018 will give him the confidence he needs to make a go of it.

Sara Sherwood was born in 1989 in South Wales and grew up in Dewsbury, West Yorkshire. She is currently working on her first novel. She can be found on Twitter @sarasherwood, and writes about books on her TinyLetter, Young Adult Affliction: tinyletter.com/sarasherwood.

Alison Thompson is an Australian poet and short story writer who lives on the South Coast of NSW. She is a longstanding member of the Kitchen Table Poets, a group of Shoalhaven Poets who have been meeting for two decades. Her poems and stories have been published in journals and anthologies in Australia and overseas. She has two chapbooks published with PressPress – *Slow Skipping* (2008) and *In A Day It Changes* in 2018. She was recently longlisted for the 2018 University of Canberra Vice-Chancellor's International Poetry Prize.